cGRAW-HILL READING

Grammar

rade 5   Practice Book

**McGraw-Hill
School Division**

York   Farmington

CONTENTS

The Gold Coin

John Henry

It's Our World, Too

Dear Mr. Henshaw

Digging Up the Past

Grade 5/Unit 2 ASSESSMENT

Carlos and the Skunk

How to Think Like a Scientist

Island Scrapbook

The Big Storm

Catching Up With Lewis & Clark

Grade 5/Unit 4 ASSESSMENT

The Riddle

Life in Flatland

Tonweya and the Eagles

Breaker's Bridge

Cleaning Up America's Air

Grade 5/Unit 5 ASSESSMENT

Sentences

> - A **sentence** is a group of words that expresses a complete thought.
>
> - A **sentence fragment** is a group of words that does not express a complete thought.
>
> - Every sentence begins with a capital letter.
>
> - A **statement** is a sentence that tells something. It ends with a period.
>
> - A **question** is a sentence that asks something. It ends with a question mark.

Read each group of words. Place a period on the line at the end if it is a *sentence*. If it is not a sentence, leave the line blank.

1. The village was ruled by a mean lord _____

2. A young farmer and his aged mother _____

3. Could not leave his mother _____

4. The farmer hid his mother under his house _____

Place a period on the line at the end of the sentence if it is a *statement*. Place a question mark at the end of the sentence if it is a *question*.

5. Why did the farmer hide his mother _____

6. Fierce warriors came to the village _____

7. How would the village survive _____

8. Lord Higa planned to take over the village _____

Extension: Ask students to write two statements and two questions about Uchida's story. Have them discuss which part of the story their sentences cover.

1

Commands and Exclamations

> - A **command** tells or asks someone to do something. It ends with a period.
>
> - An **exclamation** shows strong feeling. It ends with an exclamation mark.

Read each sentence. Place a period on the line at the end of the sentence if it is a *command*. Place an exclamation mark at the end of the sentence if it is an *exclamation*.

1. How cruel Lord Higa is _____

2. Follow his instructions _____

3. Make a rope out of ashes _____

4. What an impossible task that would be _____

5. How quickly the villagers go to the shrine _____

6. Finish these tasks before Lord Higa comes _____

7. What fools you people are _____

8. Show me the drum that makes a sound by itself _____

9. How cleverly you have done these tasks _____

10. Wow, what a great reward the young lord has given her _____

Extension: Invite students to write a brief story (serious or humorous) about a task that seems impossible. Urge them to include two commands and two exclamations, and remind them to use the correct end mark in each sentence.

Sentences

- A **statement** is a sentence that tells something. It ends with a period.

- A **question** is a sentence that asks something. It ends with a question mark.

- A **command** tells or asks someone to do something. It ends with a period.

- An **exclamation** shows strong feeling. It ends with an exclamation mark.

Read each sentence. On the line at the end of each sentence place a period if it is a *statement* or *command*, an exclamation mark if it is an *exclamation*, or a question mark if it is a *question*.

1. Take the old people to the mountains _____

2. Why is that young lord so mean _____

3. How cold it is in the forest _____

4. The farmer hid his mother in a cave _____

5. What can we do _____

6. Please pray for help _____

7. The farmer's mother has completed the tasks _____

8. What a great thing she has done for our village _____

Extension: Have partners create a dialogue between the farmer and his mother using at least one of each type of sentence. Ask them to read it aloud to the rest of the class.

Sentence Punctuation

- Every sentence begins with a capital letter.

- A statement ends with a period.

- A question ends with a question mark.

- A command ends with a period.

- An exclamation ends with an exclamation point.

Rewrite these sentences correctly by adding a period to a statement or command, a question mark to a question, and an exclamation mark to an exclamation. Make sure each sentence starts with a capital letter.

1. the young lord looked at the three completed tasks

_____

2. how did you solve these puzzles

_____

3. what a mistake I have made

_____

4. please take these bags of gold

_____

5. how could anyone destroy such clever people

_____

Extension: Ask students to choose a television program that they enjoy. Have them write one statement, one question, one command, and one exclamation about the program.

Sentences

Read each sentence. Write whether it is meant to be a statement, a question, a command, or an exclamation. Then rewrite the sentence so that its end marks and capitalization are correct.

1. _____ Why must my mother stay in the mountains

   _____

2. _____ take all the older people away

   _____

3. _____ they cannot work any longer

   _____

4. _____ What a terror Lord Higa is

   _____

5. _____ Is there nothing for us to do

   _____

6. _____ when will we ever have a kind lord

   _____

7. _____ bring me the answers now

   _____

8. _____ lord, I have brought you the answers

   _____

9. _____ How could a poor farmer solve the puzzle

   _____

10. _____ how cleverly the woman has saved us

   _____

Sentences

> - A **statement** is a sentence that tells something.
>   It ends with a period.
>
> - A **question** is a sentence that asks something.
>   It ends with a question mark.
>
> - A **command** tells or asks someone to do something.
>   It ends with a period.
>
> - An **exclamation** shows strong feeling. It ends
>   with an exclamation mark.

Label each sentence as a statement, command, question, or exclamation.
Then write each sentence correctly. Finally, illustrate one of the sentences.

1. _____ the farmer carried his mother up the mountain

_____

2. _____ how fierce Lord Higa's warriors look

_____

3. _____ solve these tasks now

_____

4. _____ will that ant get the thread through this log

_____

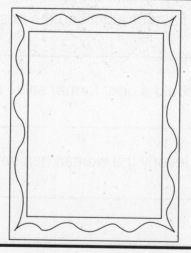

Subject

The subject of a sentence tells whom or what the sentence is about.

- The **complete subject** includes all the words in the subject.

- The **simple subject** is the main word in the complete subject. It tells exactly whom or what the sentence is about.

- You can sometimes correct a sentence fragment by adding a subject.

Read each sentence. Circle the simple subject.

1. Lucy swam toward the ship.

2. A sailor threw her a rope.

3. Caspian helped Lucy get on board.

4. The king gave his friend some dry clothes.

5. Lucy, very grateful, bowed to the young king.

Read each sentence. Circle the simple subject and underline the complete subject.

6. Lucy's cousin, Eustace cried for help.

7. The frightened boy did not want to stay on the ship.

8. The bobbing craft made him seasick.

9. The mouse, Reepicheep, disgusted him.

10. Eustace's wet clothes were cold and uncomfortable.

Extension: Have students write two sentences about the story. Ask them to circle the simple subject and underline the complete subject in each of their sentences.

Predicate

The predicate of a sentence tells what the subject does or is.

> * The **complete predicate** includes all the words in the predicate.
>
> * The **simple predicate** is the main word in the complete predicate. It tells exactly what the subject does or is.
>
> * You can sometimes correct a sentence fragment by adding a predicate.

Read each sentence. Underline the complete predicate. Circle the simple predicate.

1. Caspian rescued his friends.

2. The king gave them hot drinks.

3. He led the children to his cabin.

4. He let them borrow his clothes.

5. The friends talked all afternoon.

Read each sentence fragment. Turn the fragment into a sentence by adding a complete predicate.

6. Caspian and his crew _____

7. Lucy and Edmund _____

8. Their cousin Eustace _____

9. The mouse, Reepicheep, _____

10. The big ship _____

Extension: Have students write a few sentences about traveling on a sailing ship. Ask them to circle the simple predicate in each.

Writing Subjects and Predicates

- The **complete subject** includes all the words in the subject.

- The **simple subject** is the main word in the complete subject. It tells exactly whom or what the sentence is about.

- The **complete predicate** includes all the words in the predicate.

- The **simple predicate** is the main word in the complete predicate. It tells exactly what the subject does or is.

Read each fragment. Turn the fragment into a sentence by adding a complete subject.

1. _____ looked at the painting of the ship.

2. _____ complained about everything.

3. _____ splashed the children.

4. _____ screamed for help.

5. _____ kicked off her shoes.

Read each fragment. Turn the fragment into a sentence by adding a complete predicate.

6. Narnia, a magical land, _____

7. The king named Caspian _____

8. Reepicheep, the huge mouse, _____

9. The captain's crew _____

10. That evening, the children _____

Extension: Have students work in pairs and write four sentence fragments each. Then have them complete their partner's fragments with subjects or predicates.

Letter Punctuation

- Begin the greeting and the closing of a letter with a capital letter.

- Use a comma after the greeting in a friendly letter and the closing in all letters.

- Use a comma between the names of a city and a state.

- Use a comma between the day and year in a date.

Correct the following letter. Write capital letters where needed. Add commas where they belong.

October 9 1943
dear aunt Alberta

    You won't believe what happened to us! Edmund eustace, and I were looking at your painting. Suddenly, we were splashing in the ocean. A brave young king rescued us. Now we are sailing somewhere far away. You can leave a message for me at this address.

    P.O. Box 345
    London england

your niece
Lucy

_____

_____

_____

_____

_____

_____

_____

_____

_____

Subject and Predicate

Circle the letter for each correct answer.

1. Which of the following groups of words is a complete sentence?

    a. Eustace and his cousins.

    b. Stared at the painting.

    c. Suddenly, the waves began to move.

    d. Was sprayed in the face with salty water.

2. Which of the following groups of words is a complete sentence?

    a. Stood on the edge of the picture frame.

    b. Lucy grabbed Eustace.

    c. Lost his balance.

    d. Tumbled into the cold ocean.

3. Which sentence contains a simple subject that is underlined?

    a. Lucy liked to look at the <u>ship</u>.

    b. She was hoping to <u>visit</u> Narnia.

    c. Eustace told her to <u>take him home</u>.

    d. <u>Caspian</u> tried to cheer him up.

4. Underline the simple subject of this sentence.

    No matter how hard he tried, Eustace could not pull the painting off the wall.

5. Underline the complete subject of this sentence.

    Lucy and Edmund raced toward the moving ship.

6. Underline the simple predicate in this sentence.

    The king of Narnia paced the deck of his ship.

Subjects and Predicates

- The **complete subject** includes all the words in the subject.
- The **simple subject** is the main word in the complete subject. It tells exactly whom or what the sentence is about.
- The **complete predicate** includes all the words in the predicate.
- The **simple predicate** is the main word in the complete predicate. It tells exactly what the subject does or is.

Mechanics

- Begin the greeting and the closing of a letter with a capital letter.
- Use a comma after the greeting in a friendly letter and the closing in all letters.
- Use a comma between the names of a city and a state.
- Use a comma between the day and year in a date.

Work with a partner. Take turns reading each sentence aloud. Tell your partner the complete subject and the simple subject.

1. Lucy's clothes were drenched.

2. The boy who cried was her cousin.

3. The sailors on the ship helped the children.

4. The spray from the ocean was cold and salty.

5. Everybody was glad to see Lucy and Edmund.

Take turns reading these sentences aloud. Then write each sentence. Decide with your partner where the commas belong.

6. Lucy and Edmund visited their cousin on June 22 1942.

7. They talked about their relatives in Boise Idaho.

8. Lucy's mother was born on February 25 1925.

Sentencing Combining

> * A **conjunction** joins words or groups of words. *And*, *but*, and *or* are conjunctions.
>
> * Two related sentences can be joined with a comma and *and*, *but*, or *or*.
>
> * A sentence that contains two sentences joined by *and*, *but*, or *or* is called a **compound sentence**.

Read each pair of sentences. Rewrite them using *and*, *but*, or *or* along with a comma to make a single sentence.

1. Wilma Rudolph was a very small child. People did not think she would survive.

_____

_____

2. Wilma ran or jumped wherever she could. She was often sick.

_____

3. There was only one doctor in Clarksville who would treat black people. He was very busy.

_____

_____

4. Wilma got polio when she was almost five. The doctor said she would never be able to walk.

_____

_____

5. Wilma heard what the doctor said. She kept moving anyway.

_____

Extension: Have students work with a partner. Tell each partner to write two pairs of sentences that can be combined with *and*, *but*, or *or*. Then have each partner give his or her sentences to the other to complete.

Predicates

- You can combine two sentences by joining two subjects or two predicates with *and* or *or*.

- A **compound subject** contains two or more simple subjects that have the same predicate.

- A **compound predicate** contains two or more simple predicates that have the same subject.

Read each set of sentences. Rewrite each set as one sentence. Combine the compound subject or compound predicate in each pair with *and* or *or*.

1. The doctors helped her. Wilma's mother helped her.

_____

2. The doctors told Wilma to do her exercises. She would never walk.

_____

3. Wilma took off her brace. She walked into the church.

_____

4. Her family was amazed to see her walk. Her friends were amazed to see her walk.

_____

5. Wilma smiled when she sat down. Wilma sang when she sat down.

_____

6. Wilma could have kept the brace on. She could learn to walk without it.

_____

Extension: Ask students to write a brief story about someone who overcomes a great challenge. Have them use at least one compound subject and one compound predicate.

Grade 5/Unit 1
Wilma Unlimited 6

Sentence Combining

- A sentence that contains two sentences joined by *and*, *but*, or *or* is called a **compound sentence**.

- A **compound subject** contains two or more simple subjects that have the same predicate.

- A **compound predicate** contains two or more simple predicates that have the same subject.

Read each pair of sentences. Rewrite them using *and*, *but*, or *or* along with a comma to make a single sentence.

1. A college coach liked Wilma's basketball playing. He liked her running more.

_____

2. The coach wanted her to be on his track team. He helped her win a

scholarship.

_____

_____

3. Wilma ran track in college. She became a member of the 1960 Olympic team.

_____

4. The 1960 Olympics were held in Rome, Italy. They were the first Olympics

shown on television.

_____

_____

5. Wilma was a very fine runner. There were faster runners from other countries.

_____

_____

Extension: Have students make up pairs of
sentences that can be combined using a comma
and a conjunction or by joining a compound subject
or predicate. Then ask them to give their sentences
to another student to complete. Tell them to include
compound subjects and predicates.

Using Commas to Form Compound Sentences

- Use a comma before *and*, *but*, or *or* when you join two sentences to form a compound sentence.
- Begin every sentence with a capital letter.

When you form a compound sentence, do not begin the second part with a capital letter.

Read each group of words. Then write them correctly on the line. Be sure to use capital letters and commas in the correct places.

1. wilma was a very tiny baby and no one expected her to live.

_____

2. doctors were too expensive and her mother took care of her.

_____

3. wilma had polio and she lost the use of one leg.

_____

Read each pair of sentences. Then use a comma and *and* to combine them into one sentence. Write the new sentence on the line. Use correct capitalization.

4. Wilma loved to watch basketball. She dreamed of playing someday.

_____

5. The people in the church were thrilled to see her walk. They couldn't believe it.

_____

6. Wilma took off the brace forever. Her mother sent it back to the hospital.

_____

Extension: Have students write six examples of compound sentences joined by *and* or *but* with a comma before it.

Sentence Combining

Read the paragraph. Underline each compound sentence. Double underline any compound subjects or compound predicates.

    Wilma Rudolph is one of the most famous Olympic runners. She ran in 1960 and won three gold medals. Wilma's team won the 400-meter relay, and they came from behind to win. Wilma ran last, and when she began she was in third place. Most people thought she would never catch up. She surprised the crowd and pulled ahead at the last second. She had already won the 100-meter and 200-meter races. And she was thrilled to win three gold medals. At age five, Wilma was crippled by polio, but she became one of the fastest runners in the world. She was an inspiration to everyone.

Write a paragraph about someone you know who has had to overcome a very difficult challenge. Use five compound sentences joined by *and, but,* or *or.* Be sure to use correct capitalization and punctuation.

_____

_____

_____

_____

_____

_____

_____

Sentence Combining

- A sentence that contains two sentences joined by *and*, *but*, or *or* is called a compound sentence.

- A **compound subject** contains two or more simple subjects that have the same predicate.

- A **compound predicate** contains two or more simple predicates that have the same subject.

Mechanics

- Use a comma before *and* when you join two sentences to form a compound sentence.

- Begin every sentence with a capital letter.

Look at the picture. Then read the paragraph. Draw two lines under each letter that should be a capital letter. Put in any missing commas. Underline all compound sentences. Circle any compound subjects or predicates.

track meets are a lot of fun and there are many different events. if you like to run, there are different races. Many kids like to run and do other events. You can do the shot put or you might like to try the long jump. The pole vault and the high jump are ways to get into the air.

More Sentence Combining

- A **conjunction** joins words or groups of words.

- You can use conjunctions other than *and*, *but*, or *or* to combine sentences.

- Some conjunctions tell *where*, *when*, *why*, *how*, or *under what condition*.

Combine each pair of sentences using the conjunction in parentheses.

1. Years had passed. The *Zephyr* had been wrecked. (since)

_____

2. The boy had no fear. He was a great sailor. (because)

_____

3. The boy refused to go home. He learned to fly. (unless)

_____

4. The *Zephyr* flew. The breezes were carrying it. (as if)

_____

5. The *Zephyr* remained. It had fallen to the ground. (where)

_____

Extension: Have students write two simple sentences about the sea. Ask them to choose a conjunction from the list to combine the simple sentences.

Complex Sentences

- A sentence that contains two related ideas joined by a conjunction other than *and*, *but*, or *or* is called a **complex sentence**.

Choose the correct conjunction in parentheses that combines each pair of sentences into a new sentence that makes sense. Write the new sentence.

1. Sailors must be careful. They value their ships. (because/until)

_____

2. The waves rose. They were hills. (as though/where)

_____

3. The boy flew with the new sails. The sailor slept. (while/if)

_____

4. The *Zephyr* would fly again. He could find the island. (if/as if)

_____

5. Had the sailor dreamed it all? The boom hit his head.(whenever/when)

_____

Extension: Arrange students in pairs. Ask each student to write four simple sentences about the author's story. Then have partners use the special conjunctions to combine each other's sentences into two complex sentences.

Writing Complex Sentences

> • A sentence that contains two related ideas joined by a
> conjunction other than *and*, *but*, or *or* is called a **complex
> sentence**.

Combine each pair of complex sentences using the conjunction in
parentheses.

1. Sailors must know the sea. Their lives depend on that knowledge. (since)

_____

2. A stormy sea can toss boats. They were just toys. (as though)

_____

3. The boy could not believe his eyes. He saw two boats flying. (when)

_____

4. He would not be happy. He learned their secret. (unless)

_____

5. Flying a boat was hard. The boy never had flown before. (because)

_____

6. The boy planned to fly the *Zephyr*. He wanted to go. (wherever)

_____

7. The boy was happy. He flew over land. (when)

_____

8. The ship fell. The boy tried to keep it flying. (although)

_____

Extension: Ask students to look though a newspaper
or magazine to find examples of the conjunctions
where, *before*, *until*, *because*, *as if*, and *unless*.
Have students share and discuss the examples.

Quotations

- Use quotation marks at the beginning and end of a person's exact words.
- Begin a quotation with a capital letter.
  "The Zephyr is there on the hill," said the man.

Rewrite each sentence. Place quotation marks where they are needed. Capitalize the first letter of each quote.

1. The boy said, will you teach me? _____

2. You must promise to leave, said the sailor.

_____

3. The wind is high tonight! said the boy.

_____

4. The boy asked, where have I landed?

_____

5. Fishermen warned, never sail in a storm.

_____

6. The boy replied, I am not worried. _____

Write a dialogue between the old man and the boy. Write one part of the dialogue on each line. Be sure to place quotation marks around direct quotes, and capitalize the first letter of each quotation.

7. _____

8. _____

9. _____

10. _____

11. _____

12. _____

13. _____

14. _____

More Sentence Combining

A. Circle the letter of the sentence which is combined in the best manner.

1. Boats sail only on water. They are magic.
   - **a.** Boats sail only on water unless they are magic.
   - **b.** Boats sail only on water unless. They are magic.
   - **c.** Boats sail only on water because they are magic.

2. The *Zephyr* lay on the hill. It had been for years.
   - **a.** The *Zephyr* lay on the hill. Because it had been for years.
   - **b.** The *Zephyr* lay on the hill where it had been for years.
   - **c.** The *Zephyr* lay on the hill. Where it had been for years.

3. The boy wanted to fly the *Zephyr*. He had seen a ship fly.
   - **a.** The boy wanted to fly the *Zephyr* because he had seen a ship fly.
   - **b.** The boy wanted to fly the *Zephyr* because he had seen a ship fly.
   - **c.** The boy wanted to fly the *Zephyr* if he had seen a ship fly.

4. He knew he could fly. He practiced long enough.
   - **a.** He knew he could fly when. He practiced long enough.
   - **b.** He knew he could fly he practiced long enough.
   - **c.** He knew he could fly if he practiced long enough.

B. Circle the letter of the conjunction that best connects each sentence pair.

5. The boy dressed and went out _____ the sailor and his wife were sleeping.
   - **a.** as if
   - **b.** while
   - **c.** until

6. He flew through the night sky _____ he were a bird.
   - **a.** because
   - **b.** as if
   - **c.** before

7. The boy told his story _____ it seemed impossible.
   - **a.** although
   - **b.** unless
   - **c.** wherever

8. The man left the hill _____ he told his story.
   - **a.** if
   - **b.** unless
   - **c.** after

Conjunctions and Complex Sentences

> - You can use conjunctions other than *and*, *but*, or *or* to combine sentences.
> - Some conjunctions tell *where*, *when*, *why*, *how*, or *under what condition*.
> - A sentence that contains two related ideas joined by a conjunction other than *and*, *but*, or *or* is called a **complex sentence**.

Work with a partner. List the conjunctions that you have learned this week. Then choose a conjunction and match it with one of the following sentences. Each of you should use that conjunction to combine the sentence with a sentence of your own. (If the conjunction doesn't seem to make sense, match it with another sentence.) Write the new sentence that you both like better.

1. I visited a fishing village.

   _____

2. An old man told me a story.

   _____

3. A boy saw two boats flying.

   _____

4. Soon the Zephyr also flew.

   _____

5. The boat fell over land.

   _____

6. What would you think?

   _____

Run-On Sentences

> - A **run-on sentence** joins together two or more sentences that should be written separately.
> - You can correct a run-on sentence by separating two complete ideas into two sentences.

Correct the run-on sentences by writing two complete sentences. Remember to add capital letters and end punctuation where they are needed.

1. People want to predict the weather they have invented tools to do this.

   _____

   _____

2. Tornadoes can have winds of 330 miles per hour they can also make a lot of noise.

   _____

   _____

3. Tornado watchers drive very close to the tornado they leave an instrument to measure the storm.

   _____

   _____

4. A tornado can pick up a car and a tree a tornado can pick up boulders.

   _____

   _____

5. Scientists can watch a storm with a weather satellite these inventions have helped save lives.

   _____

   _____

6. Tornadoes mostly happen where the land is flat they happen most often in the summer or the spring.

   _____

   _____

7. Do you live where there are tornadoes we do not usually have tornadoes in California.

   _____

   _____

8. People who live in tornado territory listen to the radio they listen for a tornado watch and a tornado warning.

   _____

   _____

Extension: Ask students to proofread a partner's recent writing assignment, looking for and correcting run-on sentences.

More Run-On Sentences

> • You can correct a run-on sentence by rewriting it as a compound or complex sentence.

Correct each run-on sentence by rewriting it as a compound or complex sentence.

1. Every place has one kind of severe weather some places have more than one.

_____

_____

2. A tornado is one of the most dangerous storms no one can predict it.

_____

_____

3. People lost their homes winds picked them up like toys.

_____

4. A tornado is formed cold air mixes with warm air.

_____

5. I would like to be a tornado chaser it seems like an exciting job.

_____

6. You might hear a tornado watch you go to the Midwest in summer.

_____

7. A hurricane brings violent winds it also brings heavy rain.

_____

_____

8. Tornadoes are dangerous hurricanes are dangerous.

_____

_____

Extension: Have students write about their experiences with severe weather. Ask partners to write paragraphs that are one long run-on sentence. Have students exchange papers and correct them by writing shorter, complex, or compound sentences.

Correcting Run-On Sentences

> - A **run-on sentence** joins together two or more sentences that should be written separately.
> - You can correct a run-on sentence by separating two complete ideas into two sentences.
> - You can correct a run-on sentence by rewriting it as a compound or complex sentence.

Correct the run-on sentences. In some cases you may write two or more shorter sentences. In some cases you can rewrite the sentence as a compound or complex sentence.

1. We visited my Aunt Carole in Nebraska last summer and one Saturday there was a tornado watch and we were nervous they called it off.

_____

_____

2. Tornadoes have moved trains tornadoes have moved houses they have moved big rocks they have moved trees.

_____

3. In *The Wizard of Oz*, Dorothy's house is picked up by a tornado it is taken to the land of Oz.

_____

_____

4. The television news predicted a hurricane, Uncle George predicted a hurricane, and the weather radio in my dad's truck predicted a hurricane.

_____

_____

5. The weather seems calm today there might be a tornado they sometimes form on a day like today the weather is warm.

_____

_____

Sentence Punctuation

- Every sentence begins with a capital letter.
- Use the correct end mark for each sentence.

Read the paragraph. Rewrite the long run-on sentence correctly. Begin each sentence with a capital letter and be sure the end mark is correct.

> In the 1950s a hurricane hit the coast of Montauk, Long Island my grandparents were living there then they had a nice little house right above the beach there had been a warning my grandparents moved inland but even in the center of the island the sky grew as black as night and the winds howled fiercely Grandpa said it was the scariest thing he had ever seen the winds were so strong they created big waves that beat along the shore the sea gave some people gifts and took other people's valuable things away my grandfather was an artist and he worked in a barn near the water and when the hurricane came, the waves and wind picked up that barn and took it away they found the barn ten miles up island in East Hampton they never found the paintings that were stored in it. Grandpa was sad about that and when the storm was over, the lawn in Montauk was covered in apples there were no apple trees nearby.

_____
_____
_____
_____
_____
_____
_____
_____
_____
_____
_____

Extension: Ask students to write fictional accounts of tornadoes or hurricanes. Then have them proofread a partner's paper for capitalization and end punctuation.

28

Grade 5/Unit 1
Tornadoes!

28/12

Run-On Sentences

> - A run-on sentence joins together two or more sentences that should be written separately.
> - You can correct a run-on sentence by separating two complete ideas into two sentences
> - You can correct a run-on sentence by rewriting it as a compound or complex sentence.

A. Rewrite each run-on sentence as two or more sentences.

1. Weather tools measure temperature they are more reliable than before.

_____
_____

2. People use radar to track weather patterns radar can find a storm.

_____
_____

3. A tornado has a center it is called a vortex.

_____
_____

4. Tornado chasing is an exciting job it is not for everyone.

_____
_____

B. Rewrite each run-on sentence as a compound or complex sentence.

5. A tornado is formed when warm air crashes into hot air the wind begins to spin.

_____
_____

6. You can see a tornado coming across the plains the land is flat.

_____

7. A tornado is not predictable a tornado is not safe it is not fun.

_____

8. It's not easy to get away from a tornado you are warned ahead of time.

_____
_____

Sentence Punctuation

- Every sentence begins with a capital letter.
- Use the correct end mark for each sentence.

Read the sentences about the picture. Rewrite the run-on sentences as two separate sentences. Use a capital letter to begin each new sentence. Be sure you complete each sentence with the correct end mark.

1. The sky is dark there is a big storm today.

_____

2. A tornado is coming run for your lives!

_____

3. This tornado is gray it has picked up dirt.

_____

4. There is a tornado watch you should listen for a warning.

_____

5. The tornado is made of spinning winds the winds are very fast.

_____

Sentences

Read each passage and look at the underlined passage. Could it be written a better way? If so, which choice is best? Circle the letter of your answer.

<u>one day a fisherman caught a fish</u> The fish promised to grant him a wish if
     (1)
the man would only throw him back. <u>this was truly amazing</u> What kind of a
                                        (2)
fish was this? The man was a good man, so he threw the fish back. When he

returned home, his wife was very angry. She yelled and screamed. She

demanded that her husband go back and get his wish.

---

1. **A.** One day a fisherman caught a fish?
   B. One day a fisherman caught a fish.
   C. one day a fisherman caught a fish!
   D. No mistake.

2. **F.** This was truly amazing
   G. this was truly amazing
   H. This was truly amazing!
   J. No mistake.

Skunks live in North America. <u>Live together in rock piles</u>. <u>They also in the</u>
                                                  (3)
<u>abandoned burrows of other animals</u>. They eat rodents, insects, plants, and
           (4)
dead animals. Skunks are related to weasels, ferrets, otters, and minks.

When they are frightened or angry they spray a strong odor from a gland

under the tail.

---

3. **A.** Skunks live together in rock piles.
   B. Live together in rock piles sometimes.
   C. Often live together in rock piles
   D. No mistake.

4. **F.** They also sleep in the abandoned burrows of other animals.
   G. Also sleep in the abandoned burrows of other animals.
   H. They also sleep.
   J. No mistake.

Sentences

> The Olympics are an ancient tradition. They are now held every four years.
> (5)
> The first Olympics began in Greece in 776 B.C. Today there are many kinds
> of competitions. At first there were only running races. The games were
> (6)
> stopped at the end of the 4th century A.D., but they were started again in
> Athens in 1896.

5. A. The Olympics are an ancient tradition and they are now held every four years.
   B. The Olympics are an ancient tradition, and they are now held every four years.
   C. The Olympics are an ancient tradition, are now held every four years.
   D. No mistake.

6. F. Today there are many kinds of competitions but, at first there were only running races.
   G. Today there are many kinds of competitions, but at first there were only running races.
   H. Today there are many kinds of competitions and at first there were only running races.
   J. No mistake.

> We set sail quietly. The moon was starting to rise. Clouds gathered on the
> (7)
> horizon, but we thought nothing of it. We knew we could sail there was rain
> (8)
> or not. The winds arose when we least expected it. The waves became like
> small hills. Then they grew into giant mountains and deep valleys.

7. A. We set sail quietly so the moon was starting to rise.
   B. We set sail quietly, the moon was starting to rise.
   C. We set sail quietly as the moon was starting to rise.
   D. No mistake.

8. F. We knew we could sail whether there was rain or not.
   G. We knew we could sail as if there was rain or not.
   H. We knew we could sail, there was rain or not.
   J. No mistake.

Common and Proper Nouns

- A **noun** names a person, place, or thing.

- A **common noun** names any person, place, or thing.

- A **proper noun** names a particular person, place, or thing.

- A proper noun begins with a capital letter.

Underline each common noun on the list. Circle each proper noun.

thief	face	Juan	coin	richest
world	my	forced	Doña Josefa	hut
window	looking	man	grandfather	now
Abuelo	wife	and	wagon	house
enough	imagine	run	corn	brew

Complete each sentence by using one of the nouns from the list above.

1. The thief in "The Gold Coin" was named _____.

2. He broke into Doña Josefa's _____.

3. He was looking for a gold _____.

4. He had heard her say that she was the richest person in the _____.

5. Juan helped to harvest squash and _____ while he looked for Doña

   Josefa.

Extension: Have students work with a partner to read an article in a newspaper or magazine. Ask them to underline all the common nouns and circle all the proper nouns.

Proper Nouns With More Than One Word

> • Some proper nouns contain more than one word. Each important word begins with a capital letter.
>
> • The name of a day, month, or holiday begins with a capital letter.

Read each sentence. Then write it correctly on the line.

1. doña Josefa helped heal many people.

_____

2. One of the people she helped was don teodosio.

_____

3. She had a friend who had been to calcutta, india.

_____

4. Her friend told her about mother teresa, who also healed people.

_____

5. doña Josefa's friend told her that she was the mother teresa of their region.

_____

6. One monday in july, doña Josefa found a very sick man.

_____

7. He was from the united states of america.

_____

8. He told her that it was the fourth of july, a holiday in his country.

_____

9. By the next friday he was feeling much better.

_____

10. He hoped to return home by september for labor day.

_____

Extension: Ask students to write a short news article about someone who takes care of people who are sick. Have them include five sentences that contain a proper noun with more than one word or the name of a day, month, or holiday.

Common and Proper Nouns

- A **noun** names a person, place, or thing.

- A **common noun** names any person, place, or thing.

- A **proper noun** names a particular person, place, or thing.

- Some proper nouns contain more than one word. Each important word begins with a capital letter.

- The name of a day, month, or holiday begins with a capital letter.

Read each sentence. Underline all nouns. Underline proper nouns twice.

1. The old woman had a gold coin.

2. Juan was hoping to steal the coin.

3. Before he could steal it, Doña Josefa left her home.

4. He searched high and low but could not find any treasure.

5. Juan followed her until he came to a hut by the river.

Write a proper noun that names an example of each common noun. Include at least two examples of proper nouns that contain more than one word.

6. day of the week _____

7. month _____

8. name of a country _____

9. name of a famous athlete _____

10. university _____

11. holiday _____

12. political office _____

Extension: Ask students to work in pairs, one student naming a proper noun, such as Abraham Lincoln, and the other a common noun that names what the proper noun is - for example, president.

Abbreviations

- An **abbreviation** is the shortened form of a word.
- An abbreviation begins with a capital letter and ends with a period.
- Abbreviate titles of people before names.
- You can abbreviate the days of the week.
- You can also abbreviate most months.

Read the sentences. Fill in each blank with an abbreviation from the list.

Ms.   Dr.   Mrs.   Mr.   Jan.   Mon.   P.M.   Dec.

1. Doña Josefa will arrive this afternoon at 4 _____

2. We celebrate Christmas on _____ 25th.

3. _____ Josefa helps people who are ill.

4. Jose's wife, _____ Hernandez, is a nurse.

5. Some people call Jose _____ Hernandez.

6. On _____, July 18th, there will be a big party.

7. _____ Rodriguez also takes care of sick people.

8. _____ 1st is New Year's Day.

Read the sentences. Write the abbreviation for any word that can be abbreviated.

9. Doctor Perez will be here until six. _____

10. Celia's appointment is for August 3. _____

11. Juan was here last Tuesday. _____

12. Mister Rojas will be gone for two weeks. _____

Extension: Have students write a letter from the point of view of one of the characters in *The Gold Coin*. Encourage them to describe a scene from the story and to use at least four abbreviations.

Grade 5/Unit 2
The Gold Coin   12

Common and Proper Nouns

Rewrite each sentence. Underline each noun once. Underline proper nouns twice.

1. Doña Josefa was a very kind woman.

_____

2. She healed any person who was sick.

_____

3. She cared for Don Teodosio's wife.

_____

4. A man took her to his grandfather.

_____

5. A girl asked Doña Josefa to help her mother.

_____

6. Juan followed the woman to a farm.

_____

7. A man and a boy took him across the river in a boat.

_____

8. The boy said she had cured Abuelo with a cup of tea.

_____

Common and Proper Nouns

- A **noun** names a person, place, or thing.
- A **common noun** names any person, place, or thing.
- A **proper noun** names a particular person, place, or thing.
- A proper noun begins with a capital letter.

Mechanics

- An **abbreviation** is the shortened form of a word.
- An abbreviation begins with a capital letter and ends with a period.
- Abbreviate days of the week, most months, and titles of people before names.

Write each sentence correctly. Underline all nouns. Then write abbreviations for all words that can be abbreviated. When you are done writing, use the sentences to draw a picture.

1. on saturday, doña Josefa left her home.

_____

2. She hoped to return to her hut by wednesday.

_____

3. She was going to visit mister Gonzalez in the town of barra de navidad.

_____

4. The man had invited her to come to a party.

_____

Singular and Plural Nouns

> • A **singular noun** names one person, place, or thing.
>
> • A **plural noun** names more than one person, place, or thing.
>
> • Add -s to form the plural of most singular nouns.

Write the plural of each noun.

1. bear _____   6. mother _____

2. face _____   7. head _____

3. bed _____   8. shoulder _____

4. moon _____   9. light _____

5. animal _____   10. wing _____

Rewrite each sentence. Correct the underlined nouns.

1. All the <u>bird</u> came to see John Henry.

_____

2. John Henry cut down a whole acre of <u>tree</u>.

_____

3. John Henry's daddy gave him two <u>hammer</u>.

_____

4. When his hammers hit the rock, there were <u>chip</u> and dust everywhere.

_____

5. John Henry's <u>muscle</u> were huge and strong.

_____

Extension: Have students write five sentences about the story of John Henry. Tell them to include at least one plural noun in each sentence.

Plural Nouns with -es, -ies, and -eys

> • Add -es to form the plural of singular nouns that end in s, sh, ch, or x.
>
> • To form the plural of nouns ending in a consonant and y, change y to i and add -es.
>
> • To form the plural of nouns ending in a vowel and y, add -s.

Write the plural of each noun.

1. lady _____   6. journey _____

2. bench _____   7. fly _____

3. daddy _____   8. bush _____

4. brush _____   9. box _____

5. mix _____   10. story _____

Read each sentence. Write the correct plural for each underlined word on the line provided.

1. John Henry was one of the handsomest <u>baby</u> _____ anyone had ever seen.

2. John Henry might have had to build several <u>porch</u> _____ if he hadn't been careful.

3. Some people thought John Henry should have ridden one of the <u>pony</u> _____ in the race.

4. He's faster than a hundred <u>fox</u> _____!

5. In his travels, John Henry walked over hills and through many <u>valley</u> _____.

Extension: Have students write a dialogue between two people watching someone do something unbelievable. It could be a feat of strength as in the story, or some other amazing act. Ask them to include at least five examples of plurals of nouns that end in y, s, ch, sh, or x.

Singular and Plural Nouns

> - A **singular noun** names one person, place, or thing.
> - A **plural noun** names more than one person, place, or thing.
> - Add *-s* to form the plural of most singular nouns.
> - Add *-es* to form the plural of singular nouns that end in *s*, *sh*, *ch*, or *x*.
> - To form the plural of nouns ending in a consonant and y, change *y* to *i* and add *-es*.
> - To form the plural of nouns ending in a vowel and y, add *-s*.

Rewrite each sentence. Correct the incorrect plural forms.

1. Mamas and daddys came from all over to see John Henry.

_____

2. Many animales came to see him too.

_____

3. John Henry could run as fast as most horseies.

_____

4. He ran on roads, through bushs, and over hills.

_____

5. His daddy gave him two hammeres.

_____

6. He walked through vallies and by rivers looking for work.

_____

7. As he walked, he saw birds, flowers, and foxs.

_____

8. He passed towns with stores, churchs, and houses.

_____

9. In one yard he saw a dog with a litter of seven puppys.

_____

10. Once, he walked by a store that had lots of dresss out front.

_____

Extension: Have students quiz each other by writing sentences that incorrectly use singular nouns instead of plural nouns. Then have partners supply the correct plural form. Encourage students to write sentences about people building a railroad.

Titles

- Capitalize the first, last, and all important words in a title.
- Underline or use italics for titles of books, newspapers, magazines, or movies.
- Put quotation marks around titles of poems, short stories, songs, articles, and book chapters.

Correct each sentence. Underline titles of books, newspapers, magazines, and movies. Put quotation marks around titles of any poems, short stories, songs, articles, and book chapters. Be sure to capitalize all important words in titles.

1. Some people have never read the story, john henry.

_____

2. Marvin read about the story in the children's magazine, just for kids.

_____

3. He read that the author, Julius Lester, had also written Who I Am, Love Song, and How Many Spots Does a Leopard Have?

_____

_____

4. Another story, the red and green ribbon, was in the same issue.

_____

5. There was also an article about an old movie that had been remade, the parent trap.

_____

_____

6. Marvin decided to write a poem about John Henry's deeds, called john henry and his hammer.

_____

_____

Extension: Ask students to write five sentences that include the title of a book, magazine, short story, poem, movie, song, or other item. When they are finished, have them trade papers and check the words to be sure they have written all titles correctly.

Singular and Plural Nouns

Write the letter for each correct answer.

1. Write the letter of the incorrect plural noun. _____
   a. porches
   b. babys
   c. bushes
   d. boxes

2. Write the letter of the correct plural noun. _____
   a. monkeys
   b. foxs
   c. puppys
   d. cloudes

3. Write the letter of the incorrect plural noun. _____
   a. babies
   b. faces
   c. porches
   d. ponys

4. Write the letter of the incorrect plural noun. _____
   a. stories
   b. journies
   c. birds
   d. roses

5. Write the letter of the correct plural noun. _____
   a. patchs
   b. mixs
   c. bushes
   d. factorys

6. Write the letter of the correct plural noun. _____
   a. workeres
   b. bosses
   c. drilles
   d. trackes

Singular and Plural Nouns

- A **singular noun** names one person, place, or thing.
- A **plural noun** names more than one person, place, or thing.
- Add *-s* to form the plural of most singular nouns.
- Add *-es* to form the plural of singular nouns that end in *s*, *sh*, *ch*, or *x*.
- To form the plural of nouns ending in a consonant and *y*, change *y* to *i* and add *-es*.
- To form the plural of nouns ending in a vowel and *y*, add *-s*.

Mechanics

- A **comma** tells the reader to pause between the words that it separates.
- Use commas to separate three or more words in a series.
- Do not use a comma after the last word in a series.

Listen as your partner reads each sentence aloud. Then rewrite the sentences. Correct any incorrect nouns. Read the corrected sentences to your partner.

1. All the bird and animals watched John Henry when he was a baby.

   _____

2. Even the bears and all the rabbit came.

   _____

3. John broke all the chair on the porch.

   _____

4. John Henry used two hammer when he worked.

   _____

5. None of the other worker could do what he could do.

   _____

6. When he hammered, there were rock everywhere in the air.

   _____

More Plural Nouns

- To form the plural of most nouns ending in *f* or *fe*, add *-s*.
- For others, change the *f* to *v* and add *-es*.

Read each sentence. Write the correct form for any incorrect plural nouns on the line provided.

1. Both Dwaina and Justin are doing a lot to improve the life of people.

_____

2. Dwaina is someone who acts on her belief. _____

3. Husbands and wife can volunteer together. _____

4. Too many chief can slow a project down. _____

5. Dwaina's mother probably bought some extra chopping knife for the

volunteers to use. _____

6. Some kids help others by raking leaf. _____

7. It is important for Justin to protect his bikes from

thief. _____

8. Some people can get hungry as wolf. _____

9. Justin and Dwaina think about more than their

own self. _____

10. Volunteering with the homeless makes Dwaina realize how lucky she and

her friends are to have roof over their heads. _____

Extension: Have students write a profile of someone they know who does something to help other people. Ask students to include at least two examples of plurals of nouns that end in *f* or *fe*.

More Plural Nouns

> - To form the plural of nouns that end with a vowel and *o*, add *-s*.
> - To form the plural of nouns that end with a consonant and *o*, add *-s* or *-es*.
> - Some nouns have special plural forms.
> - A few nouns have the same singular and plural forms.

Read each sentence. Write the correct form for any incorrect plural nouns on the line provided.

1. Dwaina and her friends cut up tomatos for the sandwiches.

_____

2. While they prepare the food, they listen to two radioes. _____

3. One girl said her favorite song had three pianoes playing in it. _____

4. Someone suggested baking potatos for one of the meals.

_____

5. Many people think that kids like Dwaina and Justin are heros.

_____

6. Justin explains that it makes him feel good to help other childs.

_____

7. He knows the great feeling of getting both foots on the pedals of a bike. _____

8. A news team came to shoot videoes of him. _____

9. Dwaina says she just wants to help homeless mans, women, and kids. _____

10. Dwaina's crew works as hard as a bunch of oxes. _____

Extension: Have students work with partners to design a possible volunteer project. The project description they write should have five examples of plural nouns that end in o or have special plural forms.

Grade 5/Unit 2
It's Our World, Too! 10

Plural Nouns

- To form the plural of most nouns ending in *f* or *fe*, add *-s*.
- For others, change the *f* to *v* and add *-es*.
- To form the plural of nouns that end with a vowel and *o*, add *-s*.
- To form the plural of nouns that end with a consonant and *o*, add *-s* or *-es*.
- Some nouns have special plural forms.
- A few nouns have the same singular and plural forms.

Write the plural of each word.

1. woman _____
2. tooth _____
3. cuff _____
4. silo _____
5. leaf _____

6. deer _____
7. mouse _____
8. echo _____
9. thief _____
10. piano _____

Rewrite each sentence. Correct the underlined nouns.

11. Dwaina and her friends needed lots of bags, boxes, <u>knife</u>, and other items.
_____

12. Justin must have built a lot of <u>shelf</u> in his garage to store bike parts.
_____

13. One of Dwaina's friends thought her father might donate 20 <u>trout</u>.
_____

14. Many people heard about Justin on their <u>radio</u>. _____

15. Once they had their <u>foot</u> on the ground, both Justin and Dwaina helped a lot of people. _____

Extension: Have students write the singular and plural forms of nouns on either side of small cards. Ask them to work in pairs and quiz each other. Then have them write four sentences that use the correct plural forms of nouns ending in *-f*, *-fe*, and *o*.

Using Commas in a Series

- A **comma** tells the reader to pause between the words that it separates.
- Use commas to separate three or more words in a series.
- Do not use a comma after the last word in a series.

Correct each sentence. Add commas where they are needed.

1. Dwaina needed knives forks and spoons.

_____

2. Her friends brought radios food and bags.

_____

3. They cut tomatoes potatoes and chicken.

_____

4. They used loaves of bread jars of mayonnaise and lots of meat.

_____

5. They sliced ham turkey and cheese.

_____

6. Justin got old bikes at yard sales in thrift stores and from people.

_____

7. Justin had to clean fix and paint the old bikes.

_____

8. Often they had broken brakes seats and spokes.

_____

9. Justin asked other people for old bikes parts and money.

_____

10. Television radio and newspaper reporters came to talk to Justin.

_____

Extension: Ask students to write five sentences that each include a series of three or more words. Have them use commas correctly. Invite them to write about someone who is building or making something.

Plural Nouns

Rewrite each sentence using the correct form of each plural noun.

1. In four years, Justin Lebo has made nearly 200 bikes for childs in Paterson.

_____

2. His shelfs were packed with bike parts.

_____

3. He helped make happier lifes for a lot of kids.

_____

4. Men and womens helped him by giving him old bikes and money for parts.

_____

5. He said that people who help others aren't heros, they just enjoy what they do.

_____

6. Dwaina's friends and family helped make food for homeless mans and women.

_____

7. One friend said that it was more fun than watching videoes.

_____

8. They listened to rap music on their radioes while they worked.

_____

9. The echos of the music bounced around the kitchen.

_____

10. As they cut up meat and cheese with knifes, they talked and laughed together.

_____

Plural Nouns and Commas

- To form the plural of most nouns ending in *f* or *fe*, add *-s*.
- For others, change the *f* to *v* and add *-es*.
- To form the plural of nouns that end with a vowel and *o*, add *-s*.
- To form the plural of nouns that end with a consonant and *o*, add *-s* or *-es*.
- Some nouns have special plural forms.
- A few nouns have the same singular and plural forms.

Mechanics

- A comma tells the reader to pause between the words that it separates.
- Use commas to separate three or more words in a series.
- Do not use a comma after the last word in a series.

Look at the picture. Then read the paragraph. Find all incorrect plural nouns and write the correct forms of the plural nouns on the lines provided. Add commas to the paragraph where they are needed.

These eighth graders are helping to save a forest area. They are washing drying and waxing cars to raise money. The area they want to save has lots of animals in it. Deers, gooses, and mooses live there. There are special kinds of mouses and trouts there. Once in a while, someone sees a group of wolfs.

As the kids work, they listen to the radioes in the cars. By the end of the day the childs are tired hungry and thirsty. They are also very happy about helping to preserve a forest.

_____

_____

Possessive Nouns

- A **possessive noun** is a noun that shows who or what owns or has something.

- A **singular possessive noun** is a singular noun that shows ownership.

- Form a singular possessive noun by adding an **apostrophe (')** and an *s* to a singular noun.

Write the possessive of each noun.

1. student _____

2. librarian _____

3. man _____

4. thief _____

5. driver _____

6. Barry _____

7. mom _____

8. sister _____

9. boy _____

10. dad _____

Rewrite each sentence. Write the correct possessive for each underlined noun.

1. <u>Leigh</u> story was about his dad.

_____

2. It was about riding in his <u>father</u> truck.

_____

3. It was called "A Day on <u>Dad</u> Rig."

_____

4. Angela <u>Badger</u> books were about girls with lots of problems.

_____

5. Leigh would rather read Mr. <u>Henshaw</u> books.

_____

15 Grade 5/Unit 2
Dear Mr. Henshaw

Extension: Have students write a journal entry. Tell them to include at least three possessive nouns.

51

Plural Possessive Nouns

- A **plural possessive noun** is a plural noun that shows ownership.
- To form the possessive of a plural noun that ends in *s*, add an apostrophe.
- To form the possessive of a plural noun that does not end in *s*, add an apostrophe and *s*.

Read each sentence. Fix any incorrect possessive nouns. Write the correct answer on the line.

1. Freddys story was about a monster. _____

2. One girls poem described a still lake in the woods. _____

3. Two boys awards were honorable mentions. _____

4. Some of the girls stories were a lot like Mrs. Badger's books.

   _____

5. At the last minute, Leigh was invited to the Famous Authors lunch.

   _____

6. Mrs. Neelys car fit five people. _____

7. All the children and Angela Badger sat at the winners table.

   _____

8. The librarians sat at Mr. Badgers table. _____

9. Most of the childrens plates were filled with salad. _____

10. One boys plate only had a slice of tomato and a piece of lettuce on it.

    _____

Extension: Have students write a humorous description of a meal with six of their friends or family members. Ask them to include at least five examples of singular or plural possessive nouns.

52

Grade 5/Unit 2
Dear Mr. Henshaw /10

Singular and Plural Possessive Nouns

- A **possessive** noun is a noun that shows who or what owns or has something.
- A **singular possessive** noun is a singular noun that shows ownership.
- Form a **singular possessive** noun by adding an apostrophe (') and an *s* to a singular noun
- A **plural possessive** noun is a plural noun that shows ownership.
- To form the possessive of a plural noun that ends in *s*, add an apostrophe.
- To form the possessive of a plural noun that does not end in *s*, add an apostrophe and *s*.

Read the following paragraph. Fix all incorrect singular and plural possessive nouns.

     Leighs mother and father were divorced. Some of his friends parents also lived in separate homes. Others did not. Sometimes Leigh felt very lonely. His dads job as a trucker took him away quite a lot. Many truckers schedules are very hard. Sometimes Leigh got to ride in his fathers truck. He wrote a story about the ride. He called it "A Day on Dads Rig." One part described driving by the place where Black Barts men once watched out for travelers. They would steal the travelers valuables. Leigh entered his story in a contest with the other childrens writing.

_____

_____

_____

_____

_____

_____

_____

_____

_____

Extension: Have students write a short story that includes four examples each of singular and plural possessive nouns. Encourage them to write about one of their own experiences.

Capitalization

- A proper noun begins with a capital letter.
- The name of a day, month, or holiday begins with a capital letter.
- Capitalize the names of family members if they refer to specific people.
- Capitalize the titles of people before their names.

Correct each sentence. Rewrite any words that should be capitalized on the line.

1. leigh botts writes in his journal almost every day. _____

2. On tuesday, march 20, he wrote about trying to think up a story.

_____

3. He ended up writing a story about his father called "A day on dad's Rig."

_____

4. He was writing for the young writers' contest. _____

5. The prize was a "famous author" lunch, where he would meet a writer.

_____

6. He was hoping the author would be mr. Henshaw. _____

7. Leigh did not win first prize, but he received an honorable mention award.

_____

8. On friday, march 30, Leigh was invited to go to the lunch.

_____

9. At the lunch, he gave one of the librarians the title of super librarian.

_____

10. When Leigh got home, he said, "mom, a real author liked my story a lot."

_____

Extension: Have students write a fictional description of a meeting between a student and his or her family and the president, prince, king, or queen of another country. Encourage them to use five or more examples of words that must be capitalized, such as proper nouns like *Mom, Prince, January, Wednesday,* and *Thanksgiving.*

Grade 5/Unit 2
Dear Mr. Henshaw
10

Possessive Nouns

Rewrite each sentence using the correct form of the possessive nouns.

1. Leigh Botts diary is full of entries about his writing and his life.

_____

2. Leighs' stories are about a lot of different things.

_____

3. He wants to enter one in the Young Writer's Yearbook contest.

_____

4. Miss Neelys' words help Leigh focus on a story.

_____

5. The story tells about taking a ride in his dads truck.

_____

6. That Saturday, Leigh eats his moms' casserole with his friend Barry.

_____

7. Barry was happy to be away from his little sisters noise.

_____

8. On Monday, Miss Neely handed out the student's yearbooks.

_____

9. One girls' winning poem had been copied from a book.

_____

10. At the last minute, the schools' librarian, Miss Neely, invited Leigh to the lunch.

_____

Possessive Nouns and Capitalization

- A **possessive noun** is a noun that shows who or what owns or has something.
- A **singular possessive** noun is a singular noun that shows ownership.
- Form a singular possessive noun by adding an apostrophe (') and an *s* to a singular noun.
- A **plural possessive** noun is a plural noun that shows ownership.
- To form the possessive of a plural noun that ends in *s*, add an apostrophe.
- To form the possessive of a plural noun that does not end in *s*, add an apostrophe and *s*.

Mechanics

- A proper noun begins with a capital letter.
- The name of a day, month, or holiday begins with a capital letter.
- Capitalize the names of family members if they refer to specific people.
- Capitalize the titles of people before names.

Work with a partner. As one of you reads the first sentence aloud, the other writes it down and adds apostrophes for all possessive nouns. Then you switch parts for the next sentence. Continue until you have completed them all. Be sure that proper nouns are capitalized. Check each other's work.

1. The students stories and poems are fun to read.

_____

2. Josie is writing a story about prince williams trip to venice.

_____

3. Louis wants to tell about the time he threw out his familys photo album by mistake.

_____

_____

4. The best part is when his aunt marys friend finds it.

_____

5. Rosanne has a good idea for a story about her three cousins camping trip.

_____

Plurals and Possessives

- Do not confuse **plurals** with **possessives**.
- A **plural noun** names more than one person, place, or thing.
- Add *–s* to most nouns to form the plural. Do not use an apostrophe.

Underline each noun that names more than one person, place or thing. (Some sentences contain more than one plural noun.)

1. Jamestown's founders worked for the London Company.

2. Settlers named their town after Britain's King James.

3. Jamestown had the first colonial government for English citizens.

4. Powhatan Indians lived near the colonial fort.

5. Many colonists died of starvation and disease.

6. Visitors to Jamestown can study a model of the original fort.

7. At the park, you can watch archaeologists search under the soil.

8. Keys and beads have been found.

Extension: Have small groups of students brainstorm a list of items that are plural nouns that they might find during an archaeological dig.

Plurals and Possessives

> - A **possessive noun** shows who or what owns or has something.
> - Add an apostrophe and -s to a singular noun to make it possessive.

Read these paragraphs and study the noun choices in parentheses. In each case, draw a line under the correct noun form.

(Archaeologists/Archaeologist's) study artifacts, (object's/objects) from the past. Some (artifacts/artifact's) are tools made of iron or bone. Coins, (weapons'/weapons), or a (childs/child's) toy can also tell about life in the past.

(Worker's/Workers) at a site may not find much at first. Sometimes a (worker's/workers) tools turn up nothing, even after a (week's/weeks) work. Then (artifact's/artifacts) begin to appear. Each (object's/objects) location is recorded on a map. Soon, (scientist's/scientists) can see where and how some (tools/tool's) were used. (Skeletons/Skeleton's) near weapons may hint at a great battle. Fine (object's/objects) in a home may tell about a wealthy (family's/familys) life. (Items/Item's) from another area may help us learn about (trader's/traders).

Bill (Kelsos/Kelso's) discovery has helped people learn about Jamestown. Someday, maybe you will help your friends learn about the history of an ancient place!

Extension: Arrange students in pairs. Ask each student to write four nouns. Then have partners work together, drawing from their combined list to write four sentences. The finished sentences should contain at least two plural nouns and two possessive nouns.

Writing with Plurals and Possessives

- Do not confuse plurals with possessives.

- A **plural noun** names more than one person, place, or thing.

- Add *-s* to most nouns to form the plural. Do not use an apostrophe.

- A **possessive noun** shows who or what owns or has something.

- Add an apostrophe and *-s* to a singular noun to make it possessive.

If the underlined word in the sentence is correct, write C on the line. If the word is not correct, write it correctly.

1. Early European <u>settlement's</u> were on the coast.

_____

2. Each <u>colonists</u> family was far away.

_____

3. Settlers built daub <u>homes</u> of clay and shells.

_____

4. Native <u>American's</u> knew the land very well.

_____

5. They taught the English many farming <u>skills</u>.

_____

Extension: Challenge students to write a sentence that contains both the possessive and plural forms of the same noun. Have students compile a master list of these sentences for class discussion.

Correcting Plurals and Possessives

> - Add *-s* to most nouns to form the plural. Do not use an apostrophe.
>
> - Add an apostrophe and *-s* to a singular noun to make it possessive.
>
> - Add an apostrophe to make most plural nouns possessive.

Study each underlined noun in these paragraphs. If it is formed correctly, write **Correct** on the line with the matching number. If it is not, write the correct form.

(1) Visitor's to the National Geographic Society stare at a glass case. The **(2)** cases occupant is a skeleton! "What was this person's name?" asks one child. "I don't know" is her parent's reply.

Much about this colonist's life is a mystery. We know that he was one of the **(3)** settler's of Jamestown. Jamestown's buildings disappeared long ago. In fact, only in 1994 did **(4)** bit's of pottery reveal the **(5)** settlement's fort.

1. _____   4. _____

2. _____   5. _____

3. _____

Extension: Ask students to choose three nouns from this page and write a sentence for each noun, using either the plural or possessive form.

60

Grade 5/Unit 2
Digging Up the Past

5

Plurals and Possessives

A. Read each group of words. Write *plural* if the underlined noun names more than one person, place or thing. Write *possessive* if the underlined noun shows ownership.

1. a <u>ship's</u> sails _____

2. the <u>forts</u> in America _____

3. the <u>chief's</u> daughter _____

4. this <u>scientist's</u> discoveries _____

5. <u>diseases</u> and <u>hardships</u> _____

6. <u>artifacts</u> from Jamestown _____

B. Add apostrophes where they are needed in these sentences. If no apostrophes are needed in a sentence, write *none* after the sentence.

1. Years of hard work built the colonial towns. _____

2. This places history is truly amazing. _____

3. A historians ideas about the past sometimes include guesses.

_____

4. Archaeologists try to predict what they will find. _____

Plurals and Possessives

- A **plural noun** names more than one person, place, or thing.
- Add -s to most nouns to form the plural. Do not use an apostrophe.
- A **possessive noun** shows who or what owns or has something.
- Add an apostrophe and -s to a singular noun to make it possessive.
- Add an apostrophe to make most plural nouns possessive.

Read the sentences about this picture. Study the noun choices in parentheses. After each sentence, write the correct noun form.

1. Early Native (American/Americans) knew how to hunt and fish.

_____

2. They had (home's/homes) made of bark.

_____

3. Chief (Powhatans/Powhatan's) warriors sometimes attacked the fort.

_____

Nouns

Read the passage and look at the underlined section. Is there a mistake?
What type of mistake is it? Circle the letter of your answer.

<u>doña josefa</u> was a very wise woman. She healed people throughout the land.
        (1)
<u>On Thurs she visited Mr Gonzales</u>. He was very ill, but was feeling much
                (2)
better after she treated him.

1. **A.** Capitalization
   B. Punctuation
   C. Spelling
   D. No mistake.

2. **F.** Capitalization
   G. Punctuation
   H. Spelling
   J. No mistake.

<u>John Henry was the strongest of all the babys around</u>. Many animals came
                        (3)
to visit him. He was a fast runner. <u>He ran through bushes over hills and on
                                                    (4)
roads</u>. One time he beat a horse in a race.

3. **A.** Capitalization
   B. Punctuation
   C. Spelling
   D. No mistake.

4. **F.** Capitalization
   G. Punctuation
   H. Spelling
   J. No mistake.

Nouns

Men, womans, and childs all over the country are helping out people in need.
Justin makes bikes for kids who need them. Dwaina and her friends cook
meals for homeless people. Many people heard how Justin made happier
lifes for kids. Dwaina and Justin work so hard because they like to help, and
it makes them feel good.

5. A. Capitalization
   B. Punctuation
   C. Spelling
   D. No mistake.

6. F. Capitalization
   G. Punctuation
   H. Spelling
   J. No mistake.

Leigh entered his story in the writing contest. It was called "A Day on Dads
Rig" and was about his fathers job. The story described how they traveled
together in the truck. They drove a long way. They even passed the spot
where Black Bart's men used to steel travelers' money. Leigh got an
Honorable Mention Award for his story.

7. A. Capitalization
   B. Punctuation
   C. Spelling
   D. No mistake.

8. F. Capitalization
   G. Punctuation
   H. Spelling
   J. No mistake.

Action Verbs

- An **action verb** is a word that expresses action. It tells what the subject does or did.

- A **direct object** is a noun or pronoun that receives the action of the verb. It answers the question what? or whom? after the verb.

Underline each action verb and circle each direct object in these sentences.

1. Our school's basketball team beat our rival last week.

2. The champion player scored twelve points.

3. I made three baskets in the first half.

4. The other team missed two passes.

5. My parents watched the clock nervously.

6. How we want the pennant this year!

7. We practice difficult moves every day.

8. Julie hugged me after our victory.

9. The coach congratulated us with a big grin.

10. Put my trophy on that shelf, please.

Extension: Have partners underline examples of action verbs and circle examples of direct objects in a sports article from a newspaper.

Action Verbs

- An **action verb** is a word that expresses action. It tells what the subject does or did.

- A **direct object** is a noun or pronoun that receives the action of the verb. It answers the question *what?* or *whom?* after the verb.

Think about the story "The Marble Champ." Then complete each sentence with a word from the box that makes sense. After each sentence, write whether you added an action verb or a direct object.

marbles	squeezed	thumb	chose

1. Lupe _____ marbles as her sport. _____

2. She borrowed five _____ from her brother's collection. _____

3. Lupe strengthened her _____ through exercise. _____

4. She _____ an eraser until her hand hurt. _____

Writing Action Verbs

> - An **action verb** is a word that expresses action. It tells what the subject does or did.
> - A **direct object** is a noun or pronoun that receives the action of the verb. It answers the question what? or whom? after the verb.

Read this paragraph. Draw one line under each action verb and two lines under each direct object. (Be careful: one sentence does not have a direct object.)

Slowly I opened the can of marbles. I poured the glassy treasures onto my bedspread. Then I studied them carefully. Their beautiful colors gleamed like jewels. One marble reminded me of a pearl. I held a bright red shooter, like a ruby, in my hand. I compared two green marbles —one clear, the other cloudy. I put both into my pocket. Outside, I drew a circle in the sand. Even my brother and Alfonso praised my skill!

Write a sentence that contains each of these action verbs. Include a direct object in each sentence.

1. watched 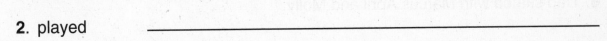 _____

2. played _____

Extension: Ask partners or groups to teach a sports skill to the class. Afterward, have the class identify four action verbs and four direct objects related to the demonstration.

Using Commas in a Series

- A comma tells the reader to pause between the words that it separates.
- Use commas to separate three or more words in a series.
- Do not use a comma after the last word in a series.

Place commas where they are needed in each sentence.

1. Ben wades surfs and snorkels.

_____

2. Lupe has learned to aim shoot and win.

_____

3. Elias Alfonso and Suzy are playing marbles.

_____

4. We will win first second or third place.

_____

5. How nervous excited and happy I feel!

_____

6. Dad skated with Marcus April and Molly.

_____

7. We like to swim dive and touch the bottom.

_____

8. Keiko dribbles shoots and steals the ball.

_____

Extension: Have volunteers suggest sentences that include commas in a series. Write the sentences on the board and have the class place commas in the series.

Action Verbs

A. Write the action verb on the line after each sentence.

1. We played marbles all weekend. _____

2. In every game, Sam beat Alisa. _____

3. Emily and I chose the prize. _____

4. Sam won a dozen chocolate chip cookies. _____

B. Add a direct object to each sentence.

5. Sam shared his _____ .

6. The next day, he had a _____ with Yoki.

7. Yoki earned two _____ right away.

8. To Sam's surprise, Yoki won the _____ .

Action Verbs

> - An **action verb** is a word that expresses action. It tells what the subject does or did.
> - A **direct object** is a noun or pronoun that receives the action of the verb. It answers the question what? or whom? after the verb.
> - A **comma** tells the reader to pause between the words that it separates.
> - Use commas to separate three or more words in a series.
> - Do not use a comma after the last word in a series.

Use commas to write each sentence correctly. Then use the sentences to draw a picture. When you are finished, describe your picture to a classmate. Try to use action verbs and direct objects in your description.

1. Lupe practiced played and improved.

_____

2. Lupe's father watched smiled and nodded.

_____

Present Tense

- A verb in the **present tense** tells what happens now.

- In the present tense, you must have **subject-verb agreement**. Add -s to most verbs if the subject is singular. Do not add -s if the subject is plural or *I* or *you*.

Complete each sentence with a present-tense verb. Make sure that the verb tells what happens now. Make sure that the verb agrees with its subject.

1. Chinese painters _____

2. Dragons _____

3. One dragon _____

4. The crowd _____

5. The people of the town _____

6. With a sigh, Mi Fei _____

7. Smoke and flames _____

8. Suddenly, the monster _____

9. The dragon _____

10. A paper lantern _____

11. Mi Fei's paper fan _____

12. His painting of the villagers _____

---

12 Grade 5/Unit 3
The Paper Dragon

Extension: Arrange students in pairs. Have partners each suggest one verb in the present tense. Then ask students to write four sentences with the same verb and different subjects.

Past Tense and Future Tense

- A verb in the past tense tells about an action that already happened.
- Add -ed to most verbs to show past tense.
- A verb in the future tense tells about an action that is going to happen.
- To write about the future, use the special verb will.

paint	murmur	laugh
learn	glow	devour
protect	roar	uncoil
wonder	scorch	climb

Complete the sentences with the past tense of one of the above verbs.

1. An artist _____ a beautiful picture.

2. I _____ about this painting from my father.

3. The girl _____ all afternoon.

4. Five dragons _____ the hillside.

5. The fire _____ dimly.

Complete the sentences with the future tense of one of the above verbs.

6. "I _____ my people," Mi Fei thought.

7. If Mi Fei fails, the dragon _____ him.

8. The artist _____ a picture of the villagers.

9. The dragon _____ with joy when he sees it.

10. I _____ about that story for the rest of my life.

Extension: Invite groups of students to write four-line poems about The Paper Dragon. Ask them to use two past tense verbs and two present tense verbs. (The poems need not rhyme.) Display the finished poems.

Grade 5/Unit 3
The Paper Dragon 10

Writing with Verb Tenses

> - A verb in the **present tense** tells what happens now. In the present tense, you must have **subject-verb agreement**. Add -s to most verbs if the subject is singular. Do not add -s if the subject is plural or *I* or *you*.
> - A verb in the **past tense** tells about an action that already happened. Add -ed to most verbs to show past tense.
> - A verb in the **future tense** tells about an action that is going to happen. To write about the future, use the special verb *will*.

Read each sentence. If the verb agrees with the subject, write *yes* on the line. If the verb does not agree, write the correct form on the line.

1. A poem tells many things. _____

2. The artist use paper for drawing. _____

3. The mountains rises high into the sky. _____

4. You fight dragons with imagination. _____

5. We solves problems every day. _____

Fill in the blank spaces using the past or future tense of one of the verbs below.

question	wonder	learn	destroy	uncoil	climb	roar

6. Last week I _____ about the end of the story.

7. Once, the dragon _____ many mulberry trees.

8. Tomorrow the artist _____ the mountain alone.

9. After he returned, the townspeople _____ him about his trip.

10. Tomorrow morning you _____ the whole story.

11. In the afternoon the dragon _____ his tail.

12. Earlier the dragon _____ loudly.

Extension: Invite students to write a message to Mi Fei, using two past and two future tense verbs. Invite volunteers to read the message aloud.

Making Spelling Changes

- If a verb ends in *s*, *ch*, *sh*, *x*, or *z*, add -*es* in the present with a singular subject.
- If a verb ends with a consonant and *y*, change *y* to *i* before adding -*es* or -*ed*.
- If a verb ends with *e*, drop the *e* before adding -*ed*.
- If a verb ends with one vowel and one consonant, double the consonant before adding -*ed*.

Read each sentence. If the underlined verb is spelled correctly, write *Correct* on the line. If the spelling is wrong, write the correct spelling.

1. Mi Fei <u>wishes</u> that the dragon would sleep. _____

2. He <u>carryes</u> his scrolls up the mountain. _____

3. The dragon's breath <u>scorchd</u> the countryside. _____

4. The fire <u>fried</u> the fields. _____

5. Mi Fei <u>careed</u> about his neighbors. _____

6. He <u>liked</u> everyone. _____

7. The people <u>worryed</u> about their crops. _____

8. The town <u>hopees</u> that Mi Fei can help. _____

9. The artist <u>mixs</u> colors with great skill. _____

10. The dragon <u>whipped</u> his giant tail. _____

11. I think that the dragon <u>tryd</u> to trick Mi Fei. _____

12. The artist's little knife <u>cliped</u> the paper. _____

13. Mi Fei <u>faned</u> wind in the dragon's face. _____

14. Mi Fei <u>fixd</u> the town's problem. _____

15. No one <u>misses</u> the dragon. _____

Extension: Bring in several books about China and distribute them to groups of students. Ask groups to locate ten verbs that follow the spelling patterns on this page. Compile a master list of the groups' responses.

Verb Tenses

A. Read each sentence. Choose the subject that agrees with the verb.
Circle the letter of the correct answer.

1. _____ fears dragons.
   a. I
   b. You
   c. The boy

2. _____ knows that love is powerful.
   a. We
   b. Children
   c. Mi Fei

3. _____ laugh very loudly.
   a. Dragons
   b. Mi Fei
   c. A man

4. _____ care about the villagers.
   a. Mi Fei
   b. Everyone
   c. You

B. Choose the correct name for the tense of the underlined verb in each sentence. Circle your answer.

5. A dragon <u>stormed</u> through the farmland.
   a. present
   b. past
   c. future

6. Now the townspeople <u>worry</u> about their fate.
   a. present
   b. past
   c. future

7. The dragon <u>whipped</u> around suddenly.
   a. present
   b. past
   c. future

8. Dragons <u>will live</u> forever in folk tales.
   a. present
   b. past
   c. future

Spelling Verbs Correctly

- A verb in the **present tense** tells what happens now. In the present tense, you must have **subject-verb agreement**. Add -s to most verbs if the subject is singular. Do not add -s if the subject is plural or *I* or *you*.
- A verb in the **past tense** tells about an action that already happened. Add -ed to most verbs to show past tense.
- A verb in the **future tense** tells about an action that is going to happen. To write about the future, use the special verb *will*.

Mechanics

- If a verb ends in *s*, *ch*, *sh*, *x*, or *z*, add -es in the present with a singular subject.
- If a verb ends with a consonant and *y*, change *y* to *i* before adding -es or -ed.
- If a verb ends with *e*, drop the *e* before adding -ed.
- If a verb ends with one vowel and one consonant, double the consonant before adding -ed.

Look at these sentences and listen as your partner reads them aloud. Then rewrite the sentences. Spell all the verbs correctly.

1. Nobody worryes about dragons these days.

   _____

2. Yesterday I tryed to make a fan.

   _____

3. The fires scorchd and wreckd the crops.

   _____

4. A boy stoped and stareed at the painting.

   _____

5. He humed a tune as he fixd his easel.

   _____

6. A bee buzzs as it flys by the box of paints.

   _____

Main and Helping Verbs

- The **main verb** in a sentence shows what the subject does or is.

- A **helping verb** helps the main verb show an action or make a statement.

- *Have*, *has*, and *had* are helping verbs.

Read the sentences. Underline the helping verb. Circle the main verb.

1. Papa had used a wagon.

2. Many families had traveled west.

3. Mama has made dresses from curtains.

4. Grandma Essie has lived to see many things.

5. Farmers everywhere have suffered from droughts.

6. The tornado had followed the river.

7. Essie had loved the Kansas house best.

8. Papa had promised them a home.

9. Grandpa has played his fiddle.

10. The children have worked many hours.

Extension: Have students write three sentences about their homes, using the helping verbs *have*, *has*, and *had* and verbs ending in -ed.

More Helping Verbs

> - *Is*, *are*, *am*, *was*, and *were* can be helping verbs.
> - *Will*, *shall*, *can*, and *could* are helping verbs.
> - Forms of *be* can be used as helping verbs. Be sure the helping verb agrees with the subject. Use *is* and *was* with a singular subject. Use *are* and *were* with a plural subject or *you*. Use *am* or *was* with *I*.

Choose a form of *be* as a helping verb in each sentence.

1. Because they wanted a new home, the pioneer family
   _____ going west.

2. I _____ reading about them in this book right now.

3. I _____ playing the mandolin last night.

4. Cows in the field _____ grazing on the grass today.

5. Yesterday the horse _____ running in the field.

6. Wild animals _____ making noise in the woods tonight.

7. Stella _____ trying to see who was coming across the field.

8. Suddenly, I _____ trying to find my father.

9. Missouri _____ becoming a tourist attraction today.

10. Dry weather and droughts _____ still causing problems for
    farmers today.

Extension: Ask partners to make a short cartoon strip about the story. Ask them to write dialogue, using each helping verb listed above.

Grade 5/Unit 3
Grandma Essie's Covered Wagon   10

Plurals and Possessives

> - The **main verb** in a sentence shows what the subject does or is.
> - A **helping verb** helps the main verb show an action or make a statement.
> - *Have, has,* and *had* are helping verbs.
> - *Is, are, am, was,* and *were* can be helping verbs.
> - *Will, shall, can,* and *could* are helping verbs.

Write a helping verb on the line.

1. Horses _____ hitched to wagons.

2. The dust _____ settling on our clothes.

3. Mama _____ make pancakes tomorrow.

4. What _____ we do about the storm?

5. Papa _____ yelling our names.

6. Right now, I _____ sitting in the wagon.

7. Right now, you _____ playing the mandolin.

Write a sentence using each helping verb.

8. (have) _____

9. (has) _____

10. (had) _____

11. (is) _____

12. (am) _____

Extension: Ask students to write a sentence about moving, using the helping verb *will.* Then have them replace the helping verb with *shall, can,* or *could,* and note the difference. Repeat with two new sentences.

Contractions

> - A contraction is a shortened form of two words.
> - A contraction can be made by combining a verb with the word *not*.
> - An apostrophe (') shows the letter *o* has been left out.

Rewrite each sentence. Write a contraction in place of the underlined words.

1. In a drought, crops <u>will not</u> grow.

_____

2. Many pioneers <u>could not</u> find steady work.

_____

3. It <u>had not</u> rained in many months.

_____

4. Children <u>did not</u> have many toys or clothes.

_____

5. Papa <u>was not</u> quitting or complaining.

_____

6. I <u>have not</u> heard my grandmother's story.

_____

7. Farmers <u>cannot</u> always trust the weather.

_____

8. <u>Do not</u> forget to ask your relatives their history.

_____

9. You <u>are not</u> walking fast enough.

_____

10. Most settlers <u>were not</u> just sitting around.

_____

11. It <u>is not</u> storming in the valleys.

_____

12. Today, the children <u>were not</u> helping to pack.

_____

Extension: Have students compare Grandma Essie's
life to their own. Ask them to write four sentences
80 using contractions.

Grade 5/Unit 3 12
Grandma Essie's Covered Wagon

Main and Helping Verbs

A. Write a main verb and a helping verb for each incomplete sentence.

1. A campfire _____ us warm.

2. The stars _____ in the sky.

3. The little children _____ .

4. You _____ when we get there.

5. Tomorrow we _____ .

B. Write a sentence using each helping verb.

6. (has) _____

7. (am) _____

8. (can) _____

9. (could) _____

10. (will) _____

Contractions

> • A contraction is a shortened form of two words.
>
> • A contraction can be made by combining a verb with the word *not*.
>
> • An apostrophe (') shows the letter *o* has been left out.

The following sentences describe the drawing above. Proofread the sentences to make sure that all contractions are spelled correctly. Write the correct spelling in the spaces.

1. The horse wont move.   _____

2. Papa isent ready yet.   _____

3. The rain clouds havnt gone away.   _____

4. All the children arent there.   _____

5. The wheel couldnt turn.   _____

Linking Verbs

> - A linking verb does not show action. It connects the subject to the rest of the sentence.
> - Common linking verbs are *am*, *is*, *are*, *was*, *were*, *will be*, *seem*, *appear*, *look*, *taste*, *feel*.

Draw one line under the subject of each sentence. Draw two lines under the linking verb in each sentence.

1. Michele Wood's ancestors were slaves

2. Today, all Americans are free.

3. Sharecropping was a difficult life.

4. The days seem shorter with music.

5. In her self-portrait, the artist looks quite proud.

Rewrite each sentence with the correct form of the linking verb *be*.

6. My grandmother always (was, am) strong.

_____

7. Her grandparents (was, were) Africans.

_____

8. My best friend's grandfather (are, is) Japanese.

_____

9. I (is, am) a violinist.

_____

10. You (are, is) a good musician, too.

_____

Extension: Have students write a note to Michele Wood. Urge them to use at least three linking verbs in their writing.

Linking Verbs

- A linking verb links the subject of a sentence to a noun or an adjective in the predicate.
- The noun or adjective that follows the linking verb names or describes the subject.

Read each sentence. Underline the word that is connected to the subject by the linking verb.

1. Today, slavery is a crime.

2. Many people's ancestors were slaves.

3. I felt proud of the courage of my ancestors.

4. You look beautiful in that picture.

5. People in our community seem very friendly, don't they?

Complete each sentence with a linking verb. Then underline the word that names or describes the subject.

6. My favorite painting _____ a self-portrait.

7. It _____ very old.

8. The colors _____ grayish.

9. The artist _____ my mother's grandfather.

10. I _____ a little nervous when I look at that picture.

11. Sometimes, it _____ alive.

12. My mother says that he _____ an interesting person.

Extension: Invite students to write and then share a paragraph about their own cultural background. Ask them to include four linking verbs in their descriptions.

Writing with Linking Verbs

> • A **linking verb** does not show action. It connects the subject to the rest of the sentence.
> • Common linking verbs are *am, is, are, was, were, will be, seem, appear, look, taste, feel.*
> • A linking verb links the subject of a sentence to a noun or an adjective in the predicate.
> • The noun or adjective that follows the linking verb names or describes the subject.

Underline the verb in each sentence. Write L if the verb is a linking verb or A if it is an action verb.

1. Our family holds a big reunion every three years. _____

2. My cousin Zena seems taller this year. _____

3. My other cousin, Renee, is a singer. _____

4. She also bakes wonderful desserts. _____

5. Her chocolate cake tastes fantastic. _____

Complete these sentences with linking verbs.

6. I _____ very excited about this party.

7. This _____ a big event, so our relatives _____ happy to come.

8. The weather _____ rather warm, doesn't it?

9. The sky _____ a little cloudy, though.

10. Our cousins _____ teenagers now, but they still come to our parties.

11. I think that they _____ glad to be here, too.

12. Tomorrow, the whole family _____ ready for the big reunion photograph.

Extension: Invite students to write a description of a relative whom they respect and admire. Ask them to use at least six linking verbs in their description.

Abbreviations

- An abbreviation is a shortenened form of a word.
- An abbreviation begins with a capital letter and ends with a period.
- Abbreviate titles of people before names. You can abbreviate days of the week.
- You can also abbreviate most months.

Write the abbreviation for each of the following words.

1. Thursday _____   6. Tuesday _____

2. October _____   7. Missus _____

3. Mister _____   8. August _____

4. Doctor _____   9. Sunday _____

5. January _____   10. February _____

Read the sentences. Underline each title of a person, month, or day of the week. After the sentences, write the abbreviations of those words.

11. Mister Yin and his wife are the oldest couple in our neighborhood.

_____

12. Mister Yin will turn 100 years old next Wednesday. _____

13. We are planning a celebration for Saturday, December 1. _____

14. The Yins have invited their good friend, Doctor Chen. _____

15. I will mail the invitations by Friday, November 23. _____

86

Extension: Have small groups of students look at newspapers for examples of these types of abbreviations and share their findings in class.

Grade 5/Unit 3
Going Back Home 15

Linking Verbs

A. Choose the linking verb that best completes the sentence. Circle the letter of the correct answer.

1. Cindy's ancestors _____ Irish.
   a. were
   b. is
   c. am
   d. was

2. She _____ proud of their culture.
   a. am
   b. were
   c. appear
   d. seems

3. Her mother _____ a Celtic dancer.
   a. am
   b. is
   c. be
   d. looks

4. She hopes that Cindy _____ a poet someday.
   a. are
   b. appear
   c. is
   d. will be

B. Choose the word that the linking verb connects to the subject of the sentence. Circle the letter of the correct answer.

5. Cindy's grandmother is a good cook.
   a. grandmother
   b. good
   c. cook
   d. Cindy's

6. Her Irish soda bread tastes wonderful.
   a. Irish
   b. soda
   c. tastes
   d. wonderful

7. I think her home always feels comfortable.
   a. comfortable
   b. home
   c. her
   d. always

8. Her flower garden will be a beautiful sight this spring.
   a. garden
   b. beautiful
   c. spring
   d. sight

Linking Verbs and Abbreviations

> • A **linking verb** does not show action. It connects the subject of a sentence to a noun or an adjective in the predicate. Common linking verbs are *am, is, are, was, were, will be, seem, appear, look, taste, feel*.

Mechanics:

> • An abbreviation is a shortened form of a word. An abbreviation begins with a capital letter and ends with a period.
>
> • Abbreviate titles of people before names. You can abbreviate days of the week and most months.

Work with a partner. Take turns reading the sentences aloud. The person who listens should add a linking verb to each sentence. Then look at the sentences together. Underline each word that could be abbreviated and write the abbreviation.

1. My uncle, Mister Robert Franklin, —————— the mayor of a

   farming town. —————

2. I —————— excited about visiting his family in December. —————

3. Uncle Bob's secretary, Miss McCoy, —————— interesting. —————

4. Last Monday she —————— glad to help us get plane tickets.—————

5. "This —————— his first airplane flight?" Doctor Reynolds asked my

   mother. —————

6. Mom —————— pleased when she told me on Tuesday, September 20.

   —————

Irregular Verbs

> • An **irregular verb** is a verb that does not add *-ed* to form the past tense.

Rewrite the paragraph. Change all the incorrect verbs to their correct past tense form.

> Plans for a sculpture of Crazy Horse begin over sixty years ago. Standing Bear writted to an artist in 1939. He described a giant sculpture. He thinked it would be bigger than Mt. Rushmore. He choosed a spot with great rocks. He feeled it was important to honor Crazy Horse. Crazy Horse was a great chief. He leaded the Sioux in battles. He knowed about justice and fairness. He speaked up for the Sioux.

_____

_____

_____

_____

_____

_____

Extension: The story includes additional irregular verbs. Create a class list of irregular verbs, and add new verbs as students find them in the story and in other books they are reading.

89

Irregular Verbs

> • Some irregular verbs have special spellings when used with the helping verb *have*, *has*, or *had*.

Write the verb that correctly completes the sentence on the line. Choose the form that goes with the helping verb.

1. The sculptor had _____ work in the morning.

   (begun, began, begin)

2. A face has _____ from the rock. (growed, grown, grew)

3. Few people had _____ about Native American heroes.

   (known, knew, know)

4. Standing Bear had _____ to Mr. Ziolkowski. (spoken, spoke)

5. The artists have _____ (eaten, ate, eated) lunch early today.

6. Ziolkowski had _____ sketches to begin. (drawn, drawed, drew)

7. People have _____ history through art. (taught, teached, teach)

8. The artist has _____ the place for the memorial.

   (choosed, chosen, chose)

9. Some historians have _____ the story of Crazy Horse.

   (wrote, writed, written)

10. Soldiers had _____ the Sioux from their land. (driven, drove, drived)

11. The Sioux had once _____ free across the plains.

    (rided, ridden, rode)

12. The government had _____ the Sioux land. (took, taked, taken)

Extension: Encourage students to read library books about the Sioux. Ask them to look through the books for examples of irregular verbs. Add the words to the class list.

Name_____ Date_____

Irregular Verbs

> - An **irregular verb** is a verb that does not add *-ed* to form the past tense.
> - Some irregular verbs have special spellings when used with the helping verb *have*, *has*, or *had*.

Use the irregular verbs in parentheses to complete the sentences below. Be sure to change the verb into the correct form.

1. (teach) This story _____ us something new about history.

2. (take) In the 1800s, immigrants had _____ Indian land.

3. (ride) People once _____ for days across the open plains.

4. (read) Our class has _____ about the Sioux warriors.

5. (speak) A Native American _____ about the

Navajo in Arizona.

6. (fight) Many warriors _____ to defend their lands.

7. (begin) Many tourists have _____ to visit the huge sculpture.

8. (begin) The artist _____ the huge project before he died.

9. (write) I have _____ a report on the Anasazi Indians.

10. (stand) Crazy Horse _____ up for what he believed in.

Extension: Ask students to write poems about Crazy Horse. Suggest that they consult the class list for new irregular verbs and include three irregular verbs in their poems.

Using Commas

> - Use a comma to set off a person's name when the person is spoken to directly.
> - Use a comma after introductory words such as *yes*, *no*, and *well*.

Work with a partner. Rewrite the following sentences inserting commas where needed. Not all sentences need commas.

1. Billy: "Dad do you know who Crazy Horse was?"

_____

2. Dad: "No who was he?"

_____

3. Billy: "He was a brave chief of the Sioux nation. He tried to protect his people and their land back in the 1800s. Do you know why?"

_____

4. Dad: "Well, I guess he was trying to protect them from White settlers."

_____

5. Billy: "That's true! They are building a giant statue in South Dakota to honor him. Don't you think that's cool?"

_____

6. Dad: "Yes Billy I do!"

_____

92

Extension: Have students write and perform their own short dialogue. Emphasize correct use of commas.

Grade 5/Unit 3
A Mountain of a Monument

6

Irregular Verbs

Write the correct form of the irregular verbs in parentheses and then complete the sentences. Use the past tense in each case.

1. (ride) Crazy Horse has _____

2. (begin) The sculptor _____

3. (think) Crazy Horse had _____

4. (take) The Sioux haven't _____

5. (know) I _____

6. (grow) The sculpture has _____

7. (give) The artist has _____

8. (choose) Standing Bear _____

Review Irregular Verbs

- An **irregular verb** is a verb that does not add *-ed* to form the past tense.
- Some irregular verbs have special spellings when used with the helping verb *have*, *has*, or *had*.

Mechanics

- Use a comma to set off a person's name when the person is spoken to directly.
- Use a comma after introductory words such as *yes*, *no*, and *well*.

Present Tense		Past Tense		Past with Helping Verb	
give	take	gave	took	given	taken
fly	see	flew	saw	flown	seen
choose	run	chose	ran	chosen	run
do		did		done	

Read the sentences. Then rewrite them using the past tense.

The horse flies across the open land.

Crazy Horse sees soldiers.

The horses run like the wind.

1. _____

2. _____

3. _____

Now write the sentences again, using past tense with *have*, *had*, or *has*.

1. _____

2. _____

3. _____

Verbs

Read each passage. Choose the word or words that belongs in the space.
Circle the letter of the correct answer.

The first time I played baseball, near disaster turned to glory. The
first time I was up at bat, I hit the ball right to the center fielder who
caught it. The next time, I hit two fouls to left field, then __(1)__ out
swinging. Then, my third time up, luck was with me. I held the bat. I
kept my eye on the ball. I could feel that this time I was going to hit it.
And boy did I slam that ball! It soared over centerfield, and right over
the fence. Three players scored runs and the Santa Rosa Orioles
__(2)__ the game!

---

1. **A.** strike
   B. struck
   C. strucks
   D. striking

2. **E.** won
   F. wins
   G. wonned
   H. will win

In China, artists have traditionally painted on paper scrolls. In the
west, artists __(3)__ on stretched canvas. Using canvas pliers, the
artist stretches a piece of canvas tightly over a wooden frame. Then
she __(4)__ a coat of primer paint on the canvas.

---

3. **A.** paint
   B. paints
   C. painted
   D. painting

4. **E.** putted
   F. put
   G. puts
   H. will put

After the primer has dried, the artist will begin work. Later, she
__(5)__ a thin coat of color on the white canvas. Then she __(6)__
thicker and thicker coats of paint.

---

5. **A.** will places
   B. will place
   C. will placed
   D. will placing

6. **E.** will add
   F. will added
   G. adding
   H. will adds

Verbs

Read each passage. Choose the word or words that belong in each space. Circle the letter of the correct answer.

I __(7)__ a book about immigrants. Millions of people have immigrated to the United States through New York's Ellis Island. Many families __(8)__ for work in the city. These people stayed in the eastern cities, often forming communities with people from their homelands.

---

7. A. has read

　B. is read

　C. have read

　D. am read

8. E. is looking

　F. were looking

　G. am looking

　H. was looking

Our ancestors __(9)__ Sioux Indians. We __(10)__ proud of our heritage. We visit our relatives every summer in the Midwest. My grandfather was a very smart man.

---

9. A. were

　B. is

　C. was

　D. am

10. E. are

　F. am

　G. is

　H. was

He __(11)__ us many things about the Sioux. He told us stories of the great chiefs, like Crazy Horse. He __(12)__ so many things that people have forgotten.

---

11. A. teached

　B. taughted

　C. taught

　D. teaching

12. E. knew

　F. knowed

　G. knews

　H. know

Adjectives

- An **adjective** is a word that describes a noun and tells *what kind* or *how many*.

- An adjective can come after the noun it describes. The noun and the adjective are connected by a linking verb.

Complete each of the following sentences with one of the adjectives from the box.

doubting	strange	unbearable	shiny	foolish
uneasy	one	best	adobe	striped

1. Carlos and Gloria played in the garden where _____ chiles grew.

2. The children lived in thick-walled _____ homes.

3. In just _____ year, Carlos had grown several inches.

4. Dos Dedos had a _____ tail.

5. Gloria thought that Carlos was _____ .

6. The _____ girl told him not to believe everything he heard.

7. The smell of Carlos's clothes was _____ .

8. Carlos wore his _____ shirt and pants to church.

9. He felt _____ when Mama asked him where his shoes were.

10. People in the church made _____ faces and held their noses.

Extension: Have students write eight sentences about an embarrassing incident they have experienced. Ask them to include at least six adjectives and to circle each one.

Demonstrative Adjectives

> - A **demonstrative adjective** tells *which one*.
> - Use *this* and *that* with singular nouns. Use *these* and *those* with plural nouns.
> - *This* and *these* refer to nouns that are nearby; *that* and *those* refer to nouns that are farther away.

Read each sentence. Rewrite it using the correct form of the demonstrative adjective.

1. Carlos thought, "I wonder if this tomatoes are ripe."

   _____

2. "What is those?" Gloria yelled suddenly and pointed to a skunk.

   _____

3. Carlos said, "These is the biggest skunk I ever saw."

   _____

4. He said, "I will catch these animal."

   _____

5. "Those is a bad idea," said Gloria.

   _____

6. She watched the skunk spray Carlos and said, "These is a boy in trouble."

   _____

7. Carlos said, "This shoes smell really bad."

   _____

8. His friend said, "That pants are ruined, too."

   _____

9. Mama ordered, "Get rid of these striped creature!"

   _____

10. Carlos nodded, "These is a smelly pest."

    _____

Adjectives

> • An **adjective** is a word that describes a noun and tells *what kind* or *how many*.
> • An adjective can come after the noun it describes. The noun and the adjective are connected by a linking verb.
> • A **demonstrative adjective** tells *which* one.
> • Use *this* and *that* with singular nouns. Use *these* and *those* with plural nouns.
> • *This* and *these* refer to nouns that are nearby. *That* and *those* refer to nouns that are farther away.

Underline each adjective that is connected to a noun by a linking verb.
Circle each linking verb. Then write the noun it describes on the line.

1. Jan Romero Stevens's books about Carlos are wonderful. _____

2. *Carlos and the Squash Plant* was first.

_____

3. The Carlos series has been popular. _____

4. The books are amusing. _____

5. Their southwest setting is interesting. _____

Read each sentence. Write the correct demonstrative adjective—*this*, *that*, *these*, or *those*—in each blank space.

6. _____ book here is my favorite.

7. _____ books by the window are Pap's.

8. I wish there were more books to read like _____

Carlos books here.

9. I like _____ one over there.

10. Would you please bring me _____ one from the shelf?

Extension: Have students write a description of a favorite animal book. Ask them to include in their writing six examples of adjectives and at least two demonstrative adjectives.

Proper Adjectives

> • A proper adjective is formed from a proper noun.
> • A proper adjective begins with a capital letter.

Rewrite each sentence. Add the correct proper adjective for each underlined proper noun. Use the dictionary for help with spelling.

1. The Carlos series was written by an <u>America</u> author.

_____

2. The books often tell about <u>Mexico</u> food.

_____

3. Many foods mentioned in the books are used in <u>Italy</u> recipes.

_____

4. <u>Rome</u> cooks use tomatoes to make fine sauces.

_____

5. Tomatoes are popular in <u>Greece</u> dishes, too.

_____

6. <u>Spain</u> people also enjoy tomatoes.

_____

7. Spicy foods are liked by <u>China</u> diners and by diners in Mexico.

_____

8. Many <u>Africa</u> recipes also use spices.

_____

9. <u>France</u> cooks use spices, too.

_____

10. Spicy foods are even found in <u>England</u> restaurants.

_____

Extension: Have students write an article for a travel magazine in which they describe scenic places, food, and people in other countries. Tell them to use at least five examples of proper adjectives.

Adjectives

Add adjectives to the following sentences.

1. Carlos and Gloria have always been _____ friends.

2. They spend hours playing in their _____ garden.

3. One day, they discovered a _____ skunk.

4. _____ Carlos decided to catch the animal.

5. The _____ skunk sprayed Carlos from head to toe.

6. The odor was _____.

7. Carlos ran to the _____ river and jumped in.

8. He scrubbed and scrubbed himself and his _____ clothes.

9. He left his _____ shoes outside the door

10. Mama asked, "What is that _____ odor?"

11. The next day in church, something _____ happened.

12. Carlos felt _____ when he realized his shoes made the whole church smell.

13. "I think that Carlos's shoes are too _____ ," said Papa.

14. Papa bought Carlos a _____ pair of boots.

15. That night, Carlos ate _____ tortillas for dinner.

Adjectives

- An **adjective** is a word that describes a noun and tells *what kind* or *how many*.
- An adjective can come after the noun it describes. The noun and the adjective are connected by a linking verb.
- A **demonstrative adjective** tells which one.
- Use *this* and *that* with singular nouns. Use *these* and *those* with plural nouns.
- *This* and *these* refer to nouns that are nearby. *That* and *those* refer to nouns that are farther away.

Mechanics

- A proper adjective is formed from a proper noun.
- A proper adjective begins with a capital letter.

Use the following adjectives to help you write a paragraph about Carlos. Then draw a scene from your story below.

nervous black spicy smelly troubled tall funny best

_____

_____

_____

_____

The Articles *A*, *An*, and *The*

- The words *a*, *an*, and *the* are special adjectives called **articles**.
- Use *a* and *an* with singular nouns.
- Use *a* if the next word starts with a consonant sound.
- Use *an* if the next word starts with a vowel sound.

Rewrite each sentence, adding the correct article *a* or *an*.

1. "Someone's stealing television from the Murphys' house."

   _____

2. She saw TV repair truck through the front window.

   _____

3. Ralph saw man go back inside the Murphys' house

   _____

4. Later we learned that the thieves had stolen violin belonging to Mr. Murphy.

   _____

5. Repairman was fixing the Johnsons' TV.

   _____

6. The Murphys' house does not have burglar alarm.

   _____

7. Ralphie made observation from his sister's room.

   _____

8. Your observation was not incorrect one.

   _____

9. Having information does not always mean you will answer question correctly.

   _____

10. Bad information can lead to wrong answer.

    _____

10

Grade 5/Unit 4
How to Think Like A Scientist: Answering
Questions by the Scientific Method

Extension: Ask students to write a story about a person
that performs a brave act. When they have finished
writing, have them circle all the articles in the story.

103

The Article *The*

> - Use *the* with singular nouns that name a particular person, place, or thing.
> - Use *the* before all plural nouns.

Read each sentence. Rewrite it, adding the correct article.

1. "Someone's stealing stuff from house across the street."

_____

2. "No way! TV repair truck is out front."

_____

3. "The men are taking something besides TV."

_____

4. We heard different story from each person.

_____

5. The Johnsons didn't notice what was going on because repairman was fixing their TV.

_____

6. Almost all of neighbors were gone during the day.

_____

7. Why did two people have different answers to same observations?

_____

8. One person assumed TV truck was there for the Murphys' house.

_____

9. Other person saw things that were being stolen and knew better.

_____

10. When you know information, it does not mean you will get right answer.

_____

Extension: Ask students to write a story about a person who stops a burglary. When they have finished writing, have them circle all the articles in the story.

104

Grade 5/Unit 4
How to Think Like A Scientist: Answering Questions by the Scientific Method / 10

Articles

> - The words *a*, *an*, and *the* are special adjectives called **articles**.
> - Use *a* and *an* with singular nouns.
> - Use *a* if the next word starts with a consonant sound.
> - Use *an* if the next word starts with a vowel sound.
> - Use *the* with singular nouns that name a particular person, place, or thing.
> - Use *the* before all plural nouns.

Write *a*, *an*, or *the* on the line before each noun.

1. _____ students

2. _____ answer

3. _____ city

4. _____ telephone

5. _____ observation

6. _____ stories

7. _____ guppies

8. _____ screen

9. _____ iguana

10. _____ aquarium

Fix each incorrect article in the following sentences.

11. Are a guppies in that bowl?

_____

12. Don't always agree with a opinion of another person.

_____

13. We will have an math assignment over the weekend.

_____

14. There are many things to do instead of a assignment.

_____

15. Whenever you get a assignment, it's important to get it done on time.

_____

Extension: Have students describe a time that they or someone they know solved a mystery. For example, they might have found something that had been lost for a long time, or they might have figured out how a magician does a particular trick. Tell them to be sure they use articles correctly.

Quotations

• Use quotation marks to set off a direct quotation from the rest of the sentence.
• Use a comma before the quotation when the speaker's name comes first.
• Use a comma, a question mark, or an exclamation point to end the quotation when the speaker's name comes last.

Rewrite each sentence. Add quotation marks and commas where needed.

1. Who can name these animals asked the teacher.

_____

2. I can said Freida. _____

3. What is the name of the lizard asked Ron.

_____

4. Freida said That's an iguana. _____

5. Watch out for the fierce fish said the zookeeper.

_____

6. They will bite anything that moves he continued.

_____

7. Angelo asked What is that animal called.

_____

8. That's a mongoose said Libby. _____

9. That's right agreed the zookeeper.

_____

10. We hope you come back and show us other animals said Jason.

_____

Extension: Have students write a dialogue between two people who are looking at animals in a zoo. When they are finished writing, have them trade papers with a partner and check to be sure that all quotations are marked correctly.

106

Grade 5/Unit 4
How to Think Like A Scientist: Answering Questions By the Scientific Method 10

Articles and Quotation Marks

Add articles to the following sentences. Use quotation marks when needed.

1. We have assignment due on Monday.

   _____

2. It's math assignment.

   _____

3. Did you do math assignment, Sam? asked Ralph.

   _____

4. Yes, I also have science experiment due on Monday said Sam.

   _____

5. Almost everyone turned in assignment.

   _____

6. One boy went to movies instead.

   _____

7. He assumed teacher would forget to collect it.

   _____

8. Sometimes people want only particular answer to a question.

   _____

9. One good way to answer questions is to use scientific method.

   _____

10. Good scientists often use experiment to find out answers.

   _____

Adjectives

> - The words *a*, *an*, and *the* are special adjectives called articles.
> - Use *a* and *an* with singular nouns.
> - Use *a* if the next word starts with a consonant sound.
> - Use *an* if the next word starts with a vowel sound.
> - Use *the* with singular nouns that name a particular person, place, or thing.
> - Use *the* before all plural nouns.

Mechanics

> - Use quotation marks to set off a direct quotation from the rest of the sentence.
> - Use a comma before the quotation when the speaker's name comes first.
> - Use a comma, a question mark, or an exclamation point to end the quotation when the speaker's name comes last.

Read each sentence aloud to a partner. Have your partner add the correct articles in the appropriate place. Then write the sentences and put commas and quotation marks wherever needed.

1. Pete ran over snake with his bicycle. ———————————————

2. Jim said It's probably inner tube. ———————————————

3. The boys looked in dark for the snake. ———————————————

4. Fortunately, they each had flashlight. ———————————————

5. Soon they saw enormous gopher snake. ———————————————

6. They watched while snake crawled into the bushes.

   ———————————————

7. That's rain snake for sure said Jim. ———————————————

8. Do you really believe snake could cause rain asked Pete.

   ———————————————

9. If you put it in tree replied Jim. ———————————————

10. Anyway, my grandpa said big snake would bring rain.

    ———————————————

Adjectives That Compare

> • Add *-er* to most adjectives to compare two people, places, or things.
> • Add *-est* to most adjectives to compare more than two.

Think about the comparisons in each sentence. Then rewrite the sentence
with the correct form for each underlined adjective.

1. The morning feels <u>warm</u> today than yesterday.

   _____

2. The sun today is the <u>bright</u> I can remember.

   _____

3. This morning I noticed the <u>small</u> crabs I've ever seen.

   _____

4. They move <u>fast</u> than the sand worms.

   _____

5. One claw on the fiddler crab is <u>large</u> than the other.

   _____

6. Amy is slightly <u>tall</u> than the great blue heron.

   _____

7. About 50 years ago, the <u>large</u> hurricane ever to hit this island blew in.

   _____

8. A much <u>small</u> hurricane passed through last week.

   _____

9. After the storm, everything seemed much <u>calm</u> than the night before.

   _____

10. That day, I found the <u>blue</u> shell in the world.

    _____

11. The turtle is much <u>slow</u> than the alligator.

    _____

12. This shell is much <u>big</u> than that one.

    _____

Extension: Have students write a paragraph describing an
outdoor walk, bike ride, or camping trip. Ask them to
include in their description four adjectives that compare.

More Adjectives That Compare

- For adjectives ending in *e*, drop the *e* before adding *-er* or *-est*.
- For adjectives ending in a consonant and *y*, change the *y* to *i* before adding *-er* or *-est*.
- For one-syllable adjectives that have a single vowel before the final consonant, double the final consonant before adding *-er* or *-est*.

Read each sentence. Rewrite it with the correct adjective forms.

1. This is the smellyest shell on the beach.

_____

2. Still, it has the fineest markings of any I've seen.

_____

3. I don't think I could feel happyer than I am right now.

_____

4. The sadest day for me is the day we leave the beach.

_____

5. You know, this shell is smallest than the pink one over there.

_____

6. The prettyest shell is in the blue box.

_____

7. I think the big sand dollar is prettyer than that.

_____

8. Actually, I can't decide which is the lovelyest shell.

_____

9. Let's try to find the larger heron we've seen.

_____

10. We should start looking near the higher point on the island.

_____

Extension: Ask pairs of students to write and present a dialogue about a visit to a store or other type of market. Have them use at least six adjectives that compare the items that they see.

Grade 5/Unit 4
An Island Scrapbook   **10**

Writing with Adjectives That Compare

- Add -er to most adjectives to compare two people, places, or things.
- Add -est to most adjectives to compare more than two.
- For adjectives ending in e, drop the e before adding -er or -est.
- For adjectives ending in a consonant and y, change the y to i before adding -er or -est.
- For one-syllable adjectives that have a single vowel before the final consonant, double the final consonant before adding -er or -est.

Write both forms of each adjective below.

1. sleepy _____ _____   **6.** fast _____ _____

2. red _____ _____   **7.** skinny _____ _____

3. fine _____ _____   **8.** high _____ _____

4. salty _____ _____   **9.** mad _____ _____

5. cool _____ _____   **10.** pretty _____ _____

Find the incorrect adjectives in these sentences. Rewrite the sentences so that the adjectives are correct.

11. These are the smaller birds on the island.

_____

12. The heron is the larger bird we ever see here.

_____

13. I love to read during the hotest part of the day.

_____

14. The funnyest moment was meeting that alligator!

_____

Extension: Ask students to write a letter to a friend from a very special place, a place the student loves to be. Encourage students to explain in their letters why they like this particular place. As they write their letters, students should use adjectives that compare.

Letter Punctuation

- Begin the greeting and the closing of a letter with a capital letter.
- Use a colon after the greeting in a business letter.
- Use a comma after the closing in a letter.
- Use a comma between the names of a city and a state.
- Use a comma between the day and year in a date.

Read the short letters below. Correct all items that are incorrect.

August 10 1999

dear Jamie

I'm having a fantastic time in North Carolina. The days have been warm and sunny, and there is so much to do in the bays and ocean. Hope you are well.

always

Jake

Sept. 9 1999

Mr. Peter Johnson
112 Slate Road
Dover DE 19904

dear Sir

I am writing to urge you to do something to stop beach erosion here on the eastern islands. Please take the time to deal with this serious problem soon. Thank you very much.

Sincerely,

Megan Homer

112

Extension: Have groups of students write a business letter about a community problem. You might have them write to a government representative or local business. Ask groups to exchange and proofread letters for correct punctuation.

Grade 5/Unit 4
An Island Scrapbook 6

Adjectives That Compare

Read the sentence. Look at the adjective in parentheses. Fill in the correct form of the adjective on the line to complete the sentence.

1. We think that today's sunrise is the _____ we have ever seen. *(red)*

2. This has been the _____ month of the summer. *(sunny)*

3. July was much _____. *(foggy)*

4. Yesterday we saw the _____ of our two favorite pond turtles. *(large)*

5. The oaks are the _____ of all the trees in the forest. *(tall)*

6. During the hurricane, the wind was _____ than during the storm in May. *(loud)*

7. Afterward, the air seemed clearer, and the sky was much _____. *(blue)*

8. The days already are growing _____, aren't they? *(short)*

9. Each day I feel _____ than the day before. *(sad)*

10. We call this the _____ island in the Atlantic Ocean. *(fine)*

Adjectives That Compare

- Add *-er* to most adjectives to compare two people, places, or things. Add *-est* to most adjectives to compare more than two.

- For adjectives ending in *e*, drop the *e* before adding *-er* or *-est*. For adjectives ending in a consonant and *y*, change the *y* to *i* before adding *-er* or *-est*. For one-syllable adjectives that have a single vowel before the final consonant, double the final consonant before adding *-er* or *-est*.

Mechanics:

- Begin the greeting and the closing of a letter with a capital letter. Use a comma after the closing in a letter.

- Use a comma between the names of a city and a state and between the day and year in a date.

Read the postcard carefully. Look for errors in adjectives, commas, and capital letters. Then rewrite the postcard correctly.

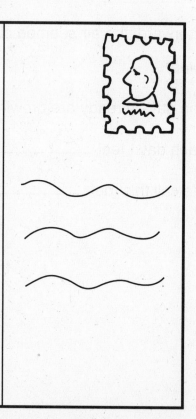

Sept. 10 1999
dear Anita
We've been having the greater time this summer. Sadly, we must leave soon. We've seen wonderful things, like the bigger heron in the world, the tinyest starfish I've ever seen, and the warmer water ever. It's even warmest than when you visited. I wish you were here now!
love
Francine

Grade 5/Unit 4
An Island Scrapbook　/10

Comparing with *More* and *Most*

> - For long adjectives, use *more* and *most* to compare people, places, and things.
> - Use *more* to compare two people, places, or things.
> - Use *most* to compare more than two.

Rewrite the sentences. Correct any adjectives that are used incorrectly.

1. Tornadoes are the more violent storms of all.

_____

2. Today's forecast is the mostest pessimistic of the entire week.

_____

3. In springtime, there is extreme weather than in fall.

_____

4. The snowdrifts were most beautiful today than yesterday.

_____

5. Avalanches are the more frightening things I have seen.

_____

6. The more stormy day this week was Saturday.

_____

7. Scientists use computers to take the exact measurements possible.

_____

8. On the coast there is a most constant stream of air than inland.

_____

Extension: Ask students to write and deliver dramatic weather reports, forecasting extreme weather with more and most.

Comparing with *More* and *Most*

- When you use *more* and *most*, do not use the ending *-er* or *-est*.

Read the paragraphs. Then rewrite each paragraph, correcting any mistakes. Be sure *more* and *most* are used correctly. Be sure all adjectives are spelled correctly.

> Where we live, the most dangerousest storms of all are tornadoes. One of the most fighteningest experiences of my life happened last April. There was a tornado watch issued. The announcer called the storm the most violentest of the season.

_____

_____

_____

_____

> We felt most vulnerable than our neighbors because our house was more exposeder than theirs was. It was on top of the more elevateder hillside in the town. I had seen what a tornado could do. They can do the more horrendous damage of any storm because they have the more extremer winds of all.

_____

_____

_____

_____

_____

Extension: Ask students to write paragraphs that continue the story. Have them use more and most with adjectives at least twice in their paragraphs.

Comparing with *More* and *Most*

> • For long adjectives, use *more* and *most* to compare people, places, and things.
> • Use *more* to compare two people, places, or things.
> • Use *most* to compare more than two.
> • When you use *more* and *most*, do not use the ending *-er* or *-est*.

Write an adjective that compares in each space. Be sure your adjectives make sense. Be sure to use *more* and *most* correctly. You may choose from the list of adjectives or use your own.

incredible	enormous	courageous	shocking
vulnerable	violent	gigantic	violent
invisible	tremendous	intense	invisible
exciting	seasonal	high-speed	enormous
amazing	important	minuscule	frightening

1. Today we heard the _____ news we'd heard all week.

2. Tornadoes have the _____ winds.

3. That weather scientist is _____ than I am.

4. I saw the _____ clouds I had ever seen.

5. The _____ droplets of water create snowflakes.

6. The _____ story this week was about a tornado and a house.

7. A tornado is _____ than a regular thunderstorm.

8. Wind is one of the _____ forces.

9. Some clouds seem _____ than mountains.

10. Avalanches are _____ than anything.

/10 Grade 5/Unit 4
The Big Storm

Extension: Ask students to write poems about the beauty and power of storms. Ask them to use more and most with adjectives at least twice in their poems.

117

Using *More* and *Most*

> • Never add *-er* and *more* to the same adjective.
> • Never add *-est* and *most* to the same adjective.

Read the sentences. If the sentence is correct, write *correct* on the line. If it is not correct, rewrite the sentence, using the correct form of the adjective.

1. A snowflake is the most prettiest thing I have ever seen.

_____

2. This avalanche was more dangerous than the last one.

_____

3. The cellar is more safer than your car.

_____

4. Weather predictions are more accurater than they used to be.

_____

5. This tornado is more unpredictable than the last one.

_____

6. The most incrediblest storm of all was in the 1980s.

_____

7. I am more cautiouser about storms than I used to be.

_____

8. We saw the most terriblest destruction of the decade.

_____

9. The tornado has the most rapidest winds of any storm.

_____

10. A weather scientist has one of the most interesting jobs.

_____

11. The tidal waves were the most enormous of the century.

_____

12. The most violentest storm last winter was off the coast.

_____

Extension: Ask partners to write four sentences about weather experiences, using *more* and *most* with adjectives. Then ask students to exchange papers, and to proofread and correct errors.

Comparing with *More* and *Most*

Circle the letter of the correct form of the adjective.

1. This is the _____ storm I have ever experienced.
   a. terriblest
   b. most terriblest
   c. most terrible

2. The clouds on the horizon are _____ than the ones above us.
   a. threateningest
   b. most threateningest
   c. more threatening

3. The rain seemed _____ every minute.
   a. most violent
   b. more violent
   c. more violenter

4. Weather prediction is the _____ job I know.
   a. more challenging
   b. challengingest
   c. most challenging

5. A tornado's winds are _____ than those of a thunderstorm.
   a. violenter
   b. most violent
   c. more violent

6. The _____ time we had was in the blizzard.
   a. excitingest
   b. most exciting
   c. most excitingest

7. That snowflake has the _____ pattern of all.
   a. more complicated
   b. most complicated
   c. complicatedest

8. You must be _____ in tornado country than here.
   a. carefuller
   b. more carefuller
   c. more careful

Comparing with *More* and *Most*

- For long adjectives, use *more* and *most* to compare people, places, and things.
- Use *more* to compare two people, places, or things.
- Use *most* to compare more than two.

Mechanics

- Never add *-er* and *more* to the same adjective.
- Never add *-est* and *most* to the same adjective.

Work with a partner. One of you reads the sentences aloud. The other proofreads. Look for the proper forms of *more* and *most* with adjectives. Take out *more* and *most* where they are not needed. Rewrite the sentences correctly.

1. Those clouds are enormouser than these are.

_____

2. The tornado was the most frighteningest one ever.

_____

3. Yesterday's sirens were the more piercing of all.

_____

4. The air near the North Pole is more frigider than anywhere.

_____

5. I think tornadoes are more better than tidal waves.

_____

6. Hailstones are more harder than snowflakes.

_____

7. Snow is more beautifuler than rain.

_____

8. I think floods are the most scariest of all disasters.

_____

Comparing with *Good*

- Use *better* to compare two people, places, or things.
- Use *best* to compare more than two.

Read each sentence. If the form of the adjective is correct, write *correct* on the line. If it is wrong, circle it and write the correct form.

1. Scientists hope to find best answers about Lewis and Clark than they have.

   _____

2. Pioneers searched for a better life than the one they left behind. _____

3. A water route would be best than a road. _____

4. Clark was Lewis's better friend of all. _____

5. A canoe is best than a sailboat for exploring inland routes. _____

6. On the best day of the trip, they spotted the ocean. _____

7. The Interpretive Center has the better exhibits of all. _____

8. Lewis and Clark searched for the better route to the Pacific. _____

9. Scientists have best clues about the route than they had ten years ago.

   _____

10. The Shoshone had the better trails of anyone. _____

11. Lewis and Clark had best horses than the Shoshone. _____

12. Sacajawea was the best guide they could have found. _____

13. The Shoshone showed the explorers bestest trails than they expected.

   _____

14. Fishing in the Pacific might be gooder than stream fishing. _____

15. Their luck might be better of all in Oregon. _____

15 Grade 5/Unit 4
Catching Up With Lewis and Clark

Extension: Ask students to write four sentences about an exploration or expedition, using the adjectives *best* and *better*.

121

Comparing with *Bad*

> • Use *worse* to compare two people, places, or things.
> • Use *worst* to compare more than two.

Rewrite the sentences, correcting forms of *good* and *bad* where necessary.

1. Lewis and Clark suffered the worse hardships in their lives.

   _____

2. Having sore feet was not the worse of their troubles.

   _____

3. Ferocious bears were one of the worser surprises on the whole trip.

   _____

4. Grizzlies seemed worst than any animal in the East.

   _____

5. In the mountains, the weather became worser than it had been.

   _____

6. Hunting was worst in the mountains than it was in the valleys.

   _____

7. The worstest part of the trip was the hunger.

   _____

8. You must be prepared for the worse conditions ever.

   _____

9. The heat is worser today than it was yesterday.

   _____

10. The worser hours of the whole day were spent hauling canoes.

   _____

Extension: Ask students to read library books about the journey of Lewis and Clark. Then ask them to write paragraphs about the explorers' worst dangers and hardships. Remind them to use worse and worst correctly.

122

Grade 5/Unit 4
Catching Up With Lewis and Clark
10

Comparing with *Good* and *Bad*

> * Use *better* to compare two people, places, or things.
> * Use *best* to compare more than two.
> * Use *worse* to compare two people, places, or things.
> * Use *worst* to compare more than two.

Read the paragraphs. Circle any errors. Rewrite each paragraph correctly in the space provided.

    We were searching for the goodest water route across America. Instead, we found a best route for some pioneers than the southern route. We followed Sacajawea, the better guide we could have hoped for. The Indians had been traveling the mountains for thousands of years. They knew gooder routes through the unfamiliar territory than we did. Their trails were the better of any we had seen.

_____

_____

_____

_____

_____

Along the way, we suffered the worstest hardships of our lives. We could not find food, and the terrain was some of the worser we had encountered. We felt worsest each day than we had the day before. The worse part of our trip was carrying the canoes. We found hiking far worst than paddling.

_____

_____

_____

_____

_____

Extension: Ask partners to write sentences about good and bad experiences in the wilderness. They can make up adventures or write about true experiences. Ask students to share their stories with the class.

Proper Adjectives

> • A proper adjective is formed from a proper noun.
>
> • A proper adjective begins with a capital letter.

Underline each proper adjective. Then write it on the line with the correct capitalization.

1. Lewis and Clark traveled across the north american continent.

_____

2. Some oregon families are descendants of pioneers. _____

3. The Rocky Mountains also cross the canadian border. _____

4. Many american families traveled Lewis and Clark's route. _____

5. One montana scientist is studying the trail of Lewis and Clark.

_____

6. At the national Memorial, there are historical exhibits. _____

7. Some of the Shoshone were english-speaking people. _____

8. It was many years until the western states joined the Union. _____

9. Lewis and Clark followed the ancient native american trails. _____

10. Many pioneers were european immigrants. _____

11. The mexican border is far from the Rocky Mountains. _____

12. The native american route turned out to be excellent. _____

Comparing with *Good* and *Bad*

A. Circle the letter of the adjective that completes the sentence correctly.

1. It was the _____ day of our entire journey.
  a. best
  b. goodest
  c. better

2. The _____ danger we encountered was the grizzly.
  a. worse
  b. worser
  c. worst

3. The view of the Pacific was the _____ thing they had ever seen.
  a. goodest
  b. better
  c. best

4. The freezing days were _____ than the hot ones.
  a. worst
  b. worse
  c. worser

5. The Oregon Trail is _____ than the California Trail.
  a. better
  b. gooder
  c. worst

B. Circle the letter of the proper adjective in each sentence.

1. Lewis and Clark crossed the Rockies near the Canadian border.
  a. Lewis
  b. Rockies
  c. Canadian

2. A Shoshone named Sacajawea led the explorers over Indian territory.
  a. Sacajawea
  b. explorers
  c. Indian

3. A Montana scientist is digging for clues.
  a. Montana
  b. scientist
  c. clues

Comparing with *Good* and *Bad*

- Use *better* to compare two people, places, or things.
- Use *best* to compare more than two.
- Use *worse* to compare two people, places, or things.
- Use *worst* to compare more than two.

Mechanics

- A proper adjective is formed from a proper noun.
- A proper adjective begins with a capital letter.

Read the sentences about the picture. Rewrite the sentences correctly.
Look for forms of the adjectives *good* and *bad*. Be sure all proper
adjectives are capitalized.

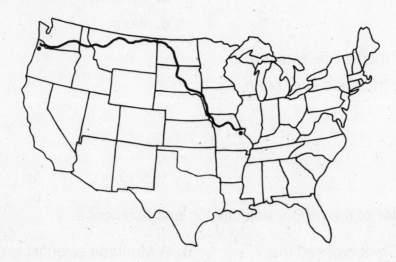

1. Which is the shorter route of all across the american continent?

_____

2. Traveling is gooder near the canadian border than it is here.

_____

3. The better trails of all were the native american ones.

_____

4. Their horses were worser than the ones we had.

_____

Adjectives

Read the passage and choose the appropriate word or group of words that belongs in each space. Circle the letter of your answer.

> The children had no idea that the picture was so real. Edmund and Lucy thought the ship looked like a ship from Narnia. But they did not realize that they were about to go on another ___(1)___ adventure. Before they knew it, they had been swept into the chilly waters and were looking up at the great green ship. They were pulled from the water by their friend Caspian, the ___(2)___ Narnian prince.

1. A. dry
   B. country
   C. exciting
   D. accidental

2. E. evil
   F. brave
   G. scary
   H. changed

> Last night, I ran over the ___(3)___ snake I ever saw. I didn't see it when I hit it. But I thought it was a snake. Pete said, "Hey, that wasn't a snake." But I thought it was. It was the ___(4)___ night in a while. We looked with our flashlights. Then we saw it. It was bigger than I imagined.

3. A. bigger
   B. biggest
   C. big
   D. most biggest

4. E. darker
   F. dark
   G. darkest
   H. most darker

> Springtime is a time of rapidly ___(5)___ weather. In the West a mass of clouds and ___(6)___, damp air rolls in off the ocean. It is the start of a big storm.

5. A. cold
   B. changing
   C. April
   D. clear

6. E. cold
   F. colder
   G. coldest
   H. most cold

Adjectives

> There are many powerful types of storms. The __(7)__ storms are tornadoes. Last year we had the most terrible storms anyone can remember. I remember one tornado that was __(8)__ than the others. It destroyed fifteen houses. Even the snow storms were the heaviest in years.

7. **A.** most powerfulest
   B. most powerfuler
   C. powefullest
   D. most powerful

8. **E.** more violenter
   F. violenter
   G. violentest
   H. more violent

> Lewis and Clark explored the American West. They were trying to find the __(9)__ route across the country. Some of the trails they found were better than others. The best were the Native American trails, though some were __(10)__ than others. With the help of Native Americans, Lewis and Clark finally reached the Pacific Ocean.

9. **A.** bestest
   B. worst
   C. best
   D. better

10. **E.** worser
   F. badder
   G. worse
   H. more bad

Pronouns

- A **pronoun** is a word that takes the place of one or more nouns.
- A pronoun must match the noun that it refers to.
- Singular pronouns are *I, you, he, she, it, me, him, her*.
- Plural pronouns are *we, you, they, us, them*.

Read these sentences and the underlined pronouns. If the pronoun is correct, write "C." If the pronoun is incorrect, write the correct pronoun.

1. The king was lost in the forest while <u>you</u> was out hunting. _____

2. The king and his horse were tired because <u>it</u> had not rested all day.

   _____

3. As he looked through the trees, the king thought, "<u>He</u> wonder what that smoke is."

   _____

4. The king asked a man, "Do <u>you</u> live here, my good fellow?" _____

5. "Yes," the man answered. "My wife and <u>her</u> live here with my mother and our

   children." _____

6. "This must be a hard life for you and <u>her</u>," said the king. _____

7. "Yes, <u>them</u> work hard, but it is not so bad," said the man. _____

8. "I have lost my men. <u>We</u> must think that I have gone home," the king explained.

   _____

9. "The king is here!" the man told his wife. "Bring <u>her</u> food and drink."

   _____

10. "I'm sorry," said the man, "but <u>him</u> don't have very much." _____

10 Grade 5/Unit 5
The Riddle

Extension: Have students briefly retell a favorite story. As they say a pronoun, have listeners raise their hands to identify it.

129

Writing Pronouns Correctly

Each sentence contains an incorrect pronoun. (There are correct pronouns in some sentences, too.) Rewrite each sentence so that all of the pronouns are correct.

1. The king looked at the charcoal maker and his family and wondered how you survived.

   _____

   _____

2. The charcoal maker looked at the king and told her that they do quite well.

   _____

   _____

3. As her stoked the fire, the charcoal maker told his story.

   _____

   _____

4. Them explained that he made just pennies a day.

   _____

   _____

5. "Even making so little," the man said, "you have more than enough."

   _____

   _____

6. The king asked, "What do I mean?"

   _____

   _____

7. The charcoal maker explained that her supports his family.

   _____

   _____

8. He said that no one gives they anything.

   _____

   _____

9. "Your Majesty, there is enough for all of you," he smiled.

   _____

   _____

10. "I are very clever indeed," the king told him.

    _____

    _____

Extension: Ask pairs of students to write and present a dialogue about meeting a famous person. Have students include examples of different kinds of pronouns in the dialogue.

Grade 5/Unit 5
The Riddle 10

Pronouns

- A **pronoun** is a word that takes the place of one or more nouns.

- A pronoun must match the noun that it refers to.

- Singular pronouns are *I, you, he, she, it, me, him, her.*

- Plural pronouns are *we, you, they, us, them.*

Think about the story "The Riddle." Then complete each sentence by writing the correct pronoun or pronouns.

1. "——————— are a very smart man," said the king to the charcoal maker.

2. The charcoal maker told his wife, "The riddle must be kept secret until ——————— have seen the king's face one hundred times."

3. The members of the court were stumped when ——————— heard the riddle.

4. None of ——————— could give the right answer.

5. One man rode until ——————— reached the charcoal maker's house.

6. "The king has given ——————— a riddle. You can help me solve ———————," he said.

7. "No, ——————— cannot help ———————," said the charcoal maker.

8. "Would this bag of gold help ——————— tell ———————?" the man asked.

9. "——————— will not help," replied the charcoal maker.

10. "Would ——————— tell me for a hundred coins?" the courtier asked ———————.

Extension: Have students look for pronouns in a passage from a favorite short story or novel. Ask them to share ten examples with a partner.

Contractions

- A contraction is a shortened form of two words.

- A contraction may be formed by combining a pronoun and a verb.

- An apostrophe shows where one or more letters have been left out.

Write the contraction for the underlined words in each sentence.

1. _____ <u>I have</u> figured out the answer.

2. _____ <u>They will</u> all wonder how I did it.

3. _____ <u>We have</u> been waiting for someone to solve the riddle.

4. _____ <u>You had</u> better have it right.

5. _____ <u>I will</u> give you the answer in just a moment.

6. _____ <u>They are</u> straining to hear!

7. _____ <u>He is</u> ready with the answer.

8. _____ <u>It is</u> not true, is it?

9. _____ <u>I am</u> waiting for the answer.

10. _____ <u>You will</u> not need to wait another moment.

Extension: Have groups of students write a news article that reports on an important event (real or imaginary) in their community. Ask them to use six or more of the contractions from this lesson.

Grade5/Unit 5
The Riddle   10

Pronouns

Rewrite each sentence so that the pronouns are correct. Also make contractions out of any pronouns and verbs that can be combined.

1. The courtier laughed when it heard the answer.

    _____

2. He said "Thank them" to the charcoal maker and then left.

    _____

3. He imagined the members of the court as she heard him give the answer.

    _____

4. He pictured the king as them made him the First Counsellor.

    _____

5. The courtier told the king, "You am looking at the new First Counsellor."

    _____

6. The king called for the charcoal maker, to punish he.

    _____

7. The king said, "Them thought you were honest, but you are not."

    _____

8. The charcoal maker explained that you had seen the king's face on one hundred

    coins.

    _____

9. The king laughed and promised, "I will give I three bags of gold."

    _____

10. "You will use one for your old age, one for your debt, and one to throw out the

    window."

    _____

Pronouns and Contractions

- A **pronoun** is a word that takes the place of one or more nouns.

- A pronoun must match the noun that it refers to.

- Singular pronouns are *I, you, he, she, it, me, him, her.*

- Plural pronouns are *we, you, they, us, them.*

Mechanics

- A contraction is a shortened form of two words.

- A contraction may be formed by combining a pronoun and a verb.

- An apostrophe shows where one or more letters have been left out.

Use the space provided to draw a picture of the king and the charcoal maker. Be sure to show how different they are. Then rewrite each sentence. Correct errors in pronouns and contractions.

1. "Im lost in the woods," the king thought as she rode along.

   _____

2. "Ill ask that man and woman if them can spare some food."

   _____

3. "They look so poor, them will not have much to eat."

   _____

4. "Them can see hes a charcoal maker."

   _____

5. "You wonder if theyre honest people," the king thought.

   _____

6. "I hate to ask they for help, but I will do it anyway."

   _____

Subject Pronouns

- Use a **subject pronoun** as the subject of a sentence.

- *I, you, he, she, it, we,* and *they* are subject pronouns.

Read each sentence. Write the correct pronoun on the line.

1. The people of Flatland know that ——————— live in only two dimensions.

2. On Earth ——————— live in three dimensions.

3. Our world would be very different if ——————— had only two dimensions.

4. If ——————— went to Flatland, you would be very confused.

5. Susie read about Flatland in a book ——————— found in the library.

6. ——————— would like to go to Flatland on my vacation.

7. Bobby said that ——————— would go with me if he could.

8. If ——————— went together, I could help him adjust to the change.

9. How would ——————— know my way around Flatland?

10. My secret is that ——————— once lived there with the triangles, squares, and

    pentagons.

Extension: Ask students to write a letter from someone in
Flatland that describes what they see and who they meet
there. Have students include at least five subject pronouns in
their letter.

Object Pronouns

- Use an **object pronoun** after an action verb or after a word such as *for, at, of, with,* or *to.*

- *Me, you, him, her, it, us,* and *them* are object pronouns.

Read each sentence. Fix each incorrect underlined pronoun by writing the correct one on the line.

1. If you give <u>I</u> a penny, I will tell how we see in Flatland. _____

2. Look at the penny from the side of <u>her</u>. _____

3. It will look to <u>they</u> like a straight line. _____

4. That's why everything looks flat to <u>we</u>. _____

5. Whatever shape I see, it looks to <u>I</u> like a line. _____

6. We have different shapes here, and we give <u>they</u> different names. _____

7. It is tricky for one of <u>we</u> to recognize another shape. _____

8. Our Farmers are equal-sided triangles, which allows <u>they</u> to plow easily.

   _____

9. I have a sharp-pointed farmer friend and have to watch out for <u>he</u>. _____

10. His wife is sharp as well, and I have to be careful with <u>she</u> too. _____

Extension: Invite students to write a brief story (serious or humorous) about a visit to Flatland. Have them include six examples of subject and object pronouns.

136

Grade 5/Unit 5
Life in Flatland
10

Subject and Object Pronouns

- Use a **subject pronoun** as the subject of a sentence.
- *I, you, he, she, it, we,* and *they* are subject pronouns.
- Use an **object pronoun** after an action verb or after a word such as *for, at, of, with,* or *to.*
- *Me, you, him, her, it, us,* and *them* are object pronouns.

Rewrite each sentence using the correct form of each incorrect pronoun.

1. Most Doctors are square, except a few of they who are pentagons.

   _____

2. Because the wisest people have so many sides, them look like a Circle.

   _____

3. Us are always careful not to bump into each other.

   _____

4. Me know a Lawyer who was hurt badly by a Soldier.

   _____

5. Him never saw the Soldier coming.

   _____

6. My friend Anne said that her once was jabbed by a Merchant.

   _____

7. It is hard to see each other, so us use our hearing to recognize another person.

   _____

8. My favorite way is by feeling, which helps I tell someone's shape.

   _____

9. I also use my sense of sight, which works pretty well for I.

   _____

10. Everyone here uses Fog because it helps we to see.

   _____

Extension: Ask students to work in small groups and write a song about Flatland. Have them include a description of the different shapes found there and use at least one example of each type of subject and object pronoun. When each group has finished its song, invite them to sing it for the class.

Using *I* and *Me*

- Always write the pronoun *I* with a capital letter.

- Use *I* or *me* last when talking about yourself and another person.

The following sentences contain some errors. Rewrite them, fixing any errors in capitalization or word order.

1. Jimmy, Leslie, and i read about Flatland.

_____

2. Me and Jimmy both read the story.

_____

3. Jimmy first told me and Leslie about Flatland.

_____

4. i couldn't really imagine what Flatland looked like.

_____

5. Leslie explained to I that there was no sun.

_____

6. I and Leslie read that it rains each day in Flatland.

_____

7. i told her that the rain always comes from the North.

_____

8. She and me read that the houses also have roofs pointing to the North.

_____

9. Jimmy, Leslie, and i want to visit Flatland.

_____

10. I and Jimmy agree that we couldn't fit.

_____

Extension: Ask students to write a journal entry that describes the strangest place they have ever visited. Have them include in their writing at least one other person. Urge them to use the pronoun correctly and to be sure they use I or me last when describing themselves and another person. Then invite them to share their writing and check each other's work for errors.

Grade 5/Unit5
Life in Flatland   /10

Subject and Object Pronouns

Circle the letter of the correct pronoun for each blank space.

1. Some of the people of Flatland are dangerous when ———— walk around.
    a. them
    b. they
    c. I
    d. me

2. The only way to avoid ———— is to be very careful.
    a. it
    b. you
    c. I
    d. them

3. ———— am a square like many Doctors and Lawyers.
    a. I
    b. you
    c. he
    d. we

4. My Merchant friend gave ———— a tip about avoiding Soldiers.
    a. she
    b. it
    c. I
    d. me

5. ———— said to always watch for their backs moving and go slow.
    a. me
    b. him
    c. she
    d. it

6. I am afraid of ———— anyway.
    a. me
    b. he
    c. them
    d. they

Subject and Object Pronouns

- Use a **subject pronoun** as the subject of a sentence.
- *I, you, he, she, it, we,* and *they* are subject pronouns.
- Use an **object pronoun** after an action verb or after a word such as *for, at, of, with,* or *to.*
- *Me, you, him, her, it, us,* and *them* are object pronouns.

Mechanics

- Always write the pronoun *I* with a capital letter.
- Use *I* or *me* last when talking about yourself and another person.

Work with a partner. Each of you read part of the paragraph aloud. Notice which words do not sound correct. Then rewrite the paragraph, correcting all errors.

Me am from Flatland. Let i tell you about my home. I and my people welcome all visitors. But visiting we is not an easy thing to do. Imagine a place with only two dimensions. Everything is flat. i and you live in very different worlds. Everyone in Flatland looks similar because us are all flat. Some are harder to see than others, like the Soldiers. i have the most trouble seeing they.

_____

_____

_____

_____

_____

_____

Pronoun-Verb Agreement

- A present-tense verb must agree with its subject pronoun.
- Add -s to most action verbs when you use the pronouns *he, she*, and *it*.
- Do not add -s to an action verb in the present tense when you use the pronouns *I, we, you*, and *they*.

Read each sentence. Fix any verbs that do not agree with their pronouns. Write the correct verb form on the line.

1. Chano listens to his father, Tasinagi, as he tell him stories of their people.

   _____

2. Chano and other young people work hard as they learns many important skills.

   _____

3. He know how to hunt buffalo. _____

4. Tasinagi watches Chano as he show him the ways of hunting deer and elk.

   _____

5. He train him in making bows and arrows. _____

6. Chano is surprised when he see his first white man. _____

7. He tells his brother, we must runs quick. _____

8. They thinks it is an evil spirit. _____

9. Tasinagi says that the white men are dangerous and that they breaks their

   promises. _____

10. But Chano's life changes when he become part of a school run by white people.

   _____

Extension: Have students write a journal entry from Chano's point of view, describing the traditional skills he learns from his father. Tell students to use five or more pronouns and to be sure that all verbs and pronouns agree.

The Verbs *Have* and *Be*

> • The verbs *have* and *be* have special forms in the present tense.

Rewrite each sentence. Correct all errors in pronoun-verb agreement.

1. I are reading about a Lakota-oyate boy named Chano.

   _____

2. He have a father and mother who teach him about his people's history.

   _____

3. He am the son of one of the leaders.

   _____

4. He have dreams of living in the old ways of his tribe.

   _____

5. But instead he are sent away from his family to a school.

   _____

6. The school is run by white people, and they has different ideas about many things.

   _____

7. Because they is not able to understand English, the Native American children do not

   trust the teachers.

   _____

   _____

8. At first, it am a very hard time for Chano.

   _____

9. After some time, he are one of the best students.

   _____

10. When he finishes school, he have a job working for the government.

   _____

Extension: Ask students to write a story about a person who must leave home to live in a new and different place. Tell them to include at least six examples of pronouns with the verbs have and be. Have them check all pronoun-verb agreement.

Grade 5/Unit 5
Tonweya and the Eagles 10

Pronoun-Verb Agreement

- A present-tense verb must agree with its subject pronoun.
- Add -s to most action verbs when you use the pronouns *he, she*, and *it*.
- Do not add -s to an action verb in the present tense when you use the pronouns *I, we, you*, and *they*.
- The verbs *have* and *be* have special forms in the present tense.

Rewrite each sentence using the correct form of each incorrect verb.

1. Chano sees two eagles as he am riding with his father and mother.

   _____

2. They is flying high in the sky.

   _____

3. Chano sees that they has red-tipped feathers.

   _____

4. His father, Tasinagi, tells him that they is the sacred birds of Tonweya.

   _____

5. His father says that it are a good sign.

   _____

6. They am the eagles who once saved Tonweya's life.

   _____

7. Chano says he want to hear the story.

   _____

8. Tasinagi tells him that it am a wonderful story.

   _____

9. Tonweya is a fine hunter, and he are a fast runner.

   _____

10. One day he am hunting when a great adventure begins.

   _____

Extension: Have students write a story in the present tense that includes some kind of bird as an important part of the plot. Tell them to use correct pronoun-verb agreement and to include the verbs have and be. When they have finished writing, have them read their stories aloud in small groups.

Capitalization

- A proper noun or proper adjective begins with a capital letter.
- Capitalize titles or abbreviations of titles when they come before the names of people.
- Capitalize the names of nationalities and languages.

Rewrite the following sentences. Fix any errors in capitalization.

1. The story of tonweya is filled with adventure.

   _____

2. He was a lakota medicine man and chief.

   _____

3. I first heard the story from my teacher, mr. grace.

   _____

4. My class was learning about native americans.

   _____

5. We learned about tribes in all parts of the united states.

   _____

6. In one class, we learned that the french called the lakota the sioux.

   _____

7. The lakota language is very different from english.

   _____

8. I enjoyed learning native american stories.

   _____

9. I especially liked the story about the boy called chano.

   _____

10. Chano was given to general pratt.

   _____

Extension: Have students write a travel article about a place they would like to visit. Direct them to include examples of proper nouns and adjectives, as well as titles or abbreviations of titles, and the names of nationalities and languages. Then have them work as a class to create a "travel magazine" that includes the different articles.

Pronoun-Verb Agreement

Read the following paragraph. Then rewrite it, correcting any errors in pronoun-verb agreement.

Tonweya is hunting buffalo when he see an eagle high overhead. He notice that she have a nest on a ledge. Tonweya hopes that it have young eaglets. He climb up and sees two birds. Letting himself down the cliff by a rope, he stand next to the birds. They screams at him. Suddenly, the rope falls and he are trapped. He have no way to escape. When the mother eagle returns, she fly round and round and then goes away. When they realizes that he won't hurt them, the eaglets is friendly. He feed them from his rawhide rope. They keeps him warm at night.

_____

_____

_____

_____

_____

_____

_____

_____

_____

_____

_____

_____

_____

Pronoun-Verb Agreement

- A present-tense verb must agree with its subject pronoun.

- Add -s to most action verbs when you use the pronouns *he, she*, and *it.*

- Do not add -s to an action verb in the present tense when you use the pronouns *I, we, you*, and *they*.

- The verbs *have* and *be* have special forms in the present tense.

Mechanics

- A proper noun or proper adjective begins with a capital letter.

- Capitalize titles or abbreviations of titles when they come before the names of people.

- Capitalize the names of nationalities and languages.

Look at the picture. Then find the pronouns in the paragraph that do not agree with verbs. Rewrite the sentences using the correct pronoun-verb agreement. Also draw two lines under each letter that should be a capital letter.

    tonweya feeds the birds and they becomes stronger. he am getting weaker and weaker. At night they sleeps close together for warmth. Each day he hope they will be able to carry him down. He have a dream and sees that he will be saved by the birds. Finally, the food is gone, and it are time to try to escape. tonweya are weak. He call the eagles to him. They come. They pick him up easily and take him to the ground.

_____

_____

_____

_____

_____

_____

Possessive Pronouns

> • A **possessive pronoun** takes the place of a possessive noun. It shows who or what owns something.
>
> • Some possessive pronouns are used before nouns (*my, your, his, her, its, our, your, their*).

Read each sentence. Fill in the missing pronoun.

1. There once was a boy who broke many of ——————— own things.

2. The emperor said to him, "I need a bridge to reach ——————— hunting palace."

3. "If you cannot build this bridge, I will have ——————— head," he told him.

4. "——————— work better be good," said the emperor.

5. As Breaker looked at the raging river, he thought he might lose ———————

   head.

6. The gorge looked very steep to ——————— eyes.

7. The river was wide, and ——————— water was deep.

8. Breaker wondered, "How does this old man know about ——————— problem?"

9. Breaker told the old man, "Here's ——————— crutch."

10. In the end, the emperor got ——————— bridge.

10

Grade 5/Unit 5
Breaker's Bridge

Extension: Have students make a drawing of how they imagine the gorge looks, including the surrounding landscape. Then ask them to write five sentences about the picture and include possessive pronouns.

147

Possessive Pronouns That Stand Alone

- Some possessive pronouns can stand alone (*mine, yours, his, hers, its, ours, yours, theirs*).

Read each sentence. Find the incorrect possessive pronoun and write it correctly on the line.

1. The emperor said, "These workers are your." _____

2. When Breaker saw the gorge, he thought, "The men may be my, but the gorge belongs to Nature." _____

3. He had his' workers bring logs and stones. _____

4. They worked until they legs were numb from cold. _____

5. The river crushed the logs and stones with all its' might. _____

6. "This river will never be our," thought Breaker. _____

7. He built a dam to stop the water from its' course. _____

8. When he heard a roar, he yelled, "The river has smashed ours dam!" _____

9. The emperor finally sent him a message, "One month only is your." _____

10. "It's mine head," thought Breaker. _____

Extension: Have students write a newspaper account of how Breaker built his bridge. Tell them to use in their writing at least four examples of possessive pronouns, including a few that stand alone. When students have finished, have them read their reports aloud in small groups.

Grade 5/Unit 5
Breaker's Bridge /10

Possessive Pronouns

- A **possessive pronoun** takes the place of a possessive noun. It shows who or what owns something.

- Some possessive pronouns are used before nouns (*my, your, his, her, its, our, your, their*).

- Some possessive pronouns can stand alone (*mine, yours, his, hers, its, ours, yours, theirs*).

Rewrite each sentence. Fix any errors you find.

1. When the dam broke, the water cleared everything in their path.

   _____

2. The two piers rocked on its foundations.

   _____

3. Each one fell over on its' side and disappeared into the water.

   _____

4. The workers thought that success would never be their.

   _____

5. "You have wasted mine money too much already," wrote the emperor.

   _____

6. "Your head will be my if I don't have the bridge in a month," he told Breaker.

   _____

7. "Yours head will be his," repeated the messenger.

   _____

8. Breaker did not want to lose his's head, but did not know what to do.

   _____

9. He saw an old man who said, "Mine gourd has the sound of souls."

   _____

10. "Your life and my are bound together," the old man said.

    _____

Extension: Ask students to write a journal entry from Breaker's point of view. Have them make the entry for the evening he meets the old man, but before he uses the pellets. Encourage students to describe Breaker's feelings about the difficulties of building the bridge.

Using Hyphens

> • Use a hyphen to show the division of a word at the end of a line. Divide the word between syllables.
> • Sometimes, you use a hyphen to connect two words to form compound words.

Choose the correct way to divide the words in these sentences. Circle your answer.

1. **a.** Breaker was afraid of the execu-

    tioner's sword.

    b. Breaker was afraid of the executi-

    oner's sword.

2. **a.** Building the bridge was a tremendo-

    us job.

    b. Building the bridge was a tremen-

    dous job.

3. **a.** Breaker became the em-

    peror's favorite bridge builder.

    b. Breaker became the empero-

    r's favorite bridge builder.

Each of these sentences contains a compound word. Rewrite the sentences, adding a hyphen to join the two parts of the compound word.

4. After the piers collapsed, Breaker didn't have much self confidence.

    _____

5. His well planned project had failed miserably.

    _____

6. Then he met a man who looked about eighty five years old.

    _____

Extension: Have students work in pairs and direct each student to write five sentences that use nouns that show possession. Then have them exchange papers and replace each possessive noun with the correct possessive pronoun.

Possessive Pronouns

Read each sentence. Then rewrite it and correct all pronoun errors.

1. Breaker rowed out to the middle of the river in his's boat.

   _____

2. The workers watched from their's places on the shore.

   _____

3. Breaker wondered if the old man's pellets would do their's job.

   _____

4. He held the first pellet in his' hand and then threw it in.

   _____

5. The water churned and rocks appeared above its' surface.

   _____

6. The river sent it's waves higher and higher.

   _____

7. The waves gradually seemed to calm they're fury.

   _____

8. Breaker reached again for he's pouch.

   _____

9. His' hands crushed the second pellet.

   _____

10. Its' power was much less than the first.

    _____

Possessive Pronouns

> • A possessive pronoun takes the place of a possessive noun. It shows who or what owns something.
>
> • Some possessive pronouns are used before nouns (*my, your, his, her, its, our, your, their*).
>
> • Some possessive pronouns can stand alone (*mine, yours, his, hers, its, ours, yours, theirs*).

> **Mechanics**
>
> • Use a hyphen to show the division of a word at the end of a line. Divide the word between syllables.
> • Sometimes, you use a hyphen to connect two words to form compound words.

Work with a partner. One reads a sentence aloud. The other proofreads it.
Correct all incorrect possessive pronouns. Look for compound words that need hyphens.

1. Breaker and his workers finished their's work.

_____

2. The emperor gave Breaker his well earned gold.

_____

3. The next winter, the river smashed the second pier with the force of it's water.

_____

4. The emperor was angry and said, "I told you to build mine bridge."

_____

5. The old man appeared and said, "You never said how long you bridge should last."

_____

_____

6. The emperor recognized the great saint and asked, "How can we serve your's needs?"

_____

_____

7. "Ours lives are all bound together," he replied and disappeared.

_____

8. The emperor probably had Breaker build more than thirty five bridges.

_____

Pronouns and Homophones

- *Its, their,* and *your* are possessive pronouns.
- *It's, they're,* and *you're* are contractions meaning *it is, they are,* and *you are.*
- Do not confuse possessive pronouns with contractions that sound the same.

Read each sentence. The underlined pronouns and contractions are used incorrectly. Write the correct usage on the line.

1. Have you ever had <u>you're</u> eyes burn from polluted air? _____

2. When <u>your</u> walking down the street, can you see a long way? _____

3. Can you smell exhaust fumes when buses pass by on <u>they're</u> routes?

   _____

4. Would you like cleaner air in <u>you're</u> community? _____

5. <u>Its</u> not an easy job, but many people are working hard on it. _____

6. One agency is the EPA, and <u>its</u> their job to set limits on pollution. _____

7. The people who work there spend <u>they're</u> days working hard on this problem.

   _____

8. <u>Its</u> their task to control sources of smog and soot. _____

9. Smog and soot can cause health problems when <u>their</u> in the air. _____

10. <u>They're</u> effects can be very harmful to peoples' eyes and lungs. _____

11. The Clean Air Act covers the tiniest bits of soot in <u>it's</u> regulations. _____

12. Companies have to figure out how to make <u>they're</u> factories cleaner. _____

12

Grade 5/Unit 5
Cleaning Up America's Air

Extension: Have students write a letter to the editor that states their point of view about air pollution. Direct them to use four examples of the pronouns and homophones presented on this page.

153

Using *There, Their,* and *They're*

- The word *there* means "in that place."
- It is easy to confuse the words *there, their,* and *they're* because they sound alike.

Rewrite each sentence. Fix each incorrect possessive pronoun.

1. Many people are worried about the effects of air pollution on they're health.

_____

2. Their are many good reasons to be concerned.

_____

3. Scientists have found in there studies that different pollutants have different effects.

_____

4. For example, cars, buses, and trucks emit carbon monoxide in they're exhaust.

_____

5. It's effects are headaches, dizziness, and heart damage.

_____

6. Doctors have seen that soot can cause breathing problems in there patients.

_____

7. They're are many deaths each year caused by air pollution.

_____

8. Some people think that they're are too many rules about air pollution.

_____

154

Extension: Ask students to write a poem about the effects of air pollution. Tell them that they can use rhymes if they like, but they do not have to. Encourage them to include several examples of the words there, their, and they're.

Grade 5/Unit 5
Cleaning Up America's Air 8

Possessive Pronouns

- *Its, their,* and *your* are possessive pronouns.
- *It's, they're,* and *you're* are contractions meaning *it is, they are,* and *you are.*
- Do not confuse possessive pronouns with contractions that sound the same.
- The word *there* means "in that place."
- It is easy to confuse the words *there, their,* and *they're* because they sound alike.

Rewrite each sentence. Change all incorrect pronouns.

1. Factories also cause many pollution problems from there emissions.

   _____

2. Its a serious problem, especially to people living near a factory.

   _____

3. But some of they're pollution travels long distances.

   _____

4. If your living near a lake in the Northeast, you may notice problems.

   _____

5. Nitrogen oxides and sulfur dioxide can mix with rain when its in the air.

   _____

6. There mixing causes acid rain, which can fall into lakes and streams.

   _____

7. When this happens, their are very bad effects on fish and wildlife.

   _____

8. Its also a serious cause of damage to trees in some areas.

   _____

Apostrophes and Possessives

- An apostrophe takes the place of letters left out of a contraction.

- Possessive pronouns do not have apostrophes.

- Do not confuse possessive pronouns with contractions.

Rewrite each of these sentences. Look for incorrect apostrophe usage and correct any errors.

1. The EPA thinks that its' a good idea to clean up the air, but it could cost $7 billion.

   _____

2. Many people believe that its well worth the cost.

   _____

3. They're work will keep a lot of people from getting sick.

   _____

4. Its most people's hope that we can live without pollution.

   _____

5. You're community will probably have cleaner air in ten years.

   _____

6. Its a shame that conditions have gotten so bad in some places.

   _____

7. Some Americans have never lived without smog in they're lives.

   _____

8. Their hoping that will change.

   _____

9. You would too if your're air made you sick.

   _____

10. One of the reasons it takes so long to change is that its expensive for some businesses.

    _____

    _____

Extension: Have students write an imaginary interview between a reporter and the head of a manufacturing business about the new environmental laws. Tell them to include examples of the pronouns and contractions covered on this page. Then have them share their work.

156

Grade 5/Unit 5
Cleaning Up America's Air
10

Pronouns and Homophones

Read each sentence. Then rewrite it, correcting any pronoun errors. If there are no errors, write "correct" on the line.

1. If your going to help clean up air pollution, there are things you can do.

   _____

2. Its not an easy job, but it's better if you start small.

   _____

3. Their are things you probably use that cause pollution.

   _____

4. Sometimes it's possible to ride a bike instead of asking for a ride in a car.

   _____

5. Sometimes your in a hurry and forget to turn off lights when you leave a room.

   _____

6. Next time, don't forget to turn off you're lights.

   _____

7. There are many more things you can do to help.

   _____

8. If you even do a little, then your helping everyone a bit.

   _____

9. The important thing is to remember to pay attention to you're actions.

   _____

10. If we all make changes, their bound to have a good effect.

    _____

11. If you're not sure where to start, do some research on conservation.

    _____

12. Their are probably some local environmental groups you can join.

    _____

Possessive Pronouns

- *Its, their*, and *your* are possessive pronouns.

- *It's, they're*, and *you're* are contractions meaning *it is, they are*, and *you are*.

- Do not confuse possessive pronouns with contractions that sound the same.

- The word *there* means "in that place."

- It is easy to confuse the words *there, their,* and *they're* because they sound alike.

Mechanics

- An apostrophe takes the place of the letters left out of a contraction.
- Possessive pronouns do not have apostrophes.

Read the sentences about the picture. Rewrite them and correct all pronoun and contraction errors.

1. Many people think that riding a bike is a great way to get where there going.

_____

2. Riding you're bike is the least polluting way to travel.

_____

3. Its good exercise, too.

_____

4. Their are other reasons to ride a bike.

_____

5. One reason is that you can avoid riding in you're car.

_____

6. But be careful! Its important to watch out for cars.

_____

Pronouns

Read the passage and look at each underlined section. Is there a mistake? If there is, how do you correct it? Circle the letter of your answer.

The King went into the forest and while hunting lost his way. <u>Finally, she found a charcoal maker and his family</u>. The man told him a riddle about his life. The King liked the riddle, and
(1)

when he left took it back to his court. He told his courtiers and asked them to solve it. <u>It all</u>
(2)

<u>tried, but only one figured out the answer</u>.

1. **A.** Add a subject.
   B. Remove the comma after "Finally."
   C. Change "she" to "he."
   D. No mistake.

2. **F.** Change "It" to "We."
   G. Change "It" to "They."
   H. Change "but" to "and."
   J. No mistake.

I just read two very different stories. <u>Them are like night and day</u>. One was called "Flatland."
(3)

The other was "Tonweya and the Eagles." The first tells about a strange place, while the other

describes a great adventure. I liked both stories a lot. <u>I gave they to my friend so that it could</u>
(4)

<u>read them, too</u>.

3. **A.** Change "Them" to "Those."
   B. Change "Them" to "That."
   C. Change "Them" to "They."
   D. No mistake.

4. **F.** Change "they" to "them" and "it" to "he."
   G. Change "it" to "he."
   H. Change "they" to "them."
   J. No mistake.

There was once a boy who was always breaking things. <u>She didn't do it on purpose</u>. He
(5)

just had very clumsy hands. <u>Them called him Breaker</u>.
(6)

5. **A.** Change "She" to "They."
   B. Change "She" to "We."
   C. Change "She" to "He."
   D. No mistake.

6. **F.** Change "Them" to "Us."
   G. Change "Them" to "They."
   H. Change "him" to "her."
   J. No mistake.

Pronouns

The emperor told Breaker that he wanted him to build a bridge. "Yours men can

build the bridge to my's hunting palace," he said. Breaker looked at the gorge in
            (7)

dismay. "I don't know if I can build his bridge," he thought. Yet, the emperor had

told Breaker that he would take his head if he failed. He will have his bridge,

Breaker decided. His workers worked their hardest. But in the end they needed
                      (8)

magic to succeed.

---

7. **A.** Change "Yours" to "You're" and "my's" to "mine."
   B. Change "Yours" to "Your" and "my's" to "me."
   C. Change "Yours" to "Your" and "my's" to "my."
   D. No mistake.

8. **F.** Change "workers" to "worker's."
   G. Change "hardest" to "harder."
   H. Change "their" to "they're."
   J. No mistake.

The EPA helps to fight pollution in the U.S. Their are serious pollution problems,
                                                      (9)

which their trying to fix. Air pollution is one of the most serious problems. It's the

cause of many diseases, particularly breathing illnesses. Many people are suffering

from this problem. However, you're one of the people who can help. Your efforts
                                (10)

can help reduce air pollution.

---

9. **A.** Change "Their" to "They're."
   B. Remove the comma from the sentence.
   C. Change "Their" to "There" and "their" to "they're."
   D. No mistake.

10. **F.** Change "you're" to "your."
    G. Change "you're" to "you."
    H. Insert a comma after "one."
    J. No mistake.

Adverbs

> • An **adverb** is a word that tells more about a verb, an adjective, or another adverb.
>
> • An adverb can tell *how*, *when*, or *where* an action takes place.

Underline the adverb in each sentence. On the line, write whether the adverb describes *how*, *when*, or *where*.

1. The slave ship slowly left the harbor. _____

2. The ship stank inside. _____

3. Spanish traders treated the slaves roughly. _____

4. Dead slaves were thrown overboard. _____

5. Stormy winds tossed the ship mercilessly. _____

6. Cinqué always thought about his wife and children. _____

7. He looked down and started planning. _____

8. Cinqué freed himself and then freed other slaves. _____

9. The men fought hard. _____

10. Later a judge sat and listened to their case. _____

11. The Africans waited nervously for his decision. _____

12. Because they were free, they gladly gave thanks. _____

12 Grade 5/Unit 6
Amistad Rising

Extension: Have students write three sentences about a historical event. Ask them to tell *where*, *when*, and *how* the event happened.

161

Adverbs

> • An adverb can describe an adjective or another adverb.

In these sentences, the adverbs describe verbs, adverbs, or adjectives.
Underline each adverb.

1. The anchor sank slowly.

2. Cinqué decided very quickly.

3. The sails were almost full.

4. I think that Cinqué acted quite bravely.

5. He and the other enslaved Africans were finally free.

Complete each sentence with an adverb that describes the underlined word. You can
choose from the adverbs in the box.

almost	very	completely	terribly	quite	rather	too

6. Slave traders acted _____ selfishly.

7. The ships fought _____ hard.

8. The skies were _____ black.

9. The stars were _____ amazing.

10. The judge will decide _____ quickly.

Extension: Ask partners to write three sentences with
at least one adverb in them. Have partners try to add
162   another adverb to each other's sentences.

Grade 5/Unit 6
Amistad Rising   10

Writing with Adverbs

> • An **adverb** is a word that tells more about a verb, an adjective, or another adverb.
>
> • An adverb can tell *how*, *when*, or *where* an action takes place.

Read the following story once. Then write adverbs in the spaces. Make sure that each adverb makes sense.

Another Fight for Freedom

Abd al-Rahman Ibrahima was _____ courageous. He was

the son of a West African chieftain. Because he was a prince, Ibrahima was educated

_____ . He _____ learned how to read

and write. He studied _____ hard to learn history, mathematics,

and Moslem traditions. One day, Dr. Cox, a white man, became _____

lost in the jungle. He _____ begged Ibrahima's people for help.

They _____ saved his life, and Ibrahima became

_____ good friends with him.

When Ibrahima was in his twenties, he _____ was captured

in a war. He was sold as a slave and _____ taken to America.

One day, Ibrahima was traveling _____ along a dirt road in

Mississippi. _____ he saw Dr. Cox. The doctor was glad to see

Ibrahima. He frowned _____ , though, when he learned that this

African prince was enslaved. Dr. Cox wrote to friends, and they _____

tried to help. They _____ gained Ibrahima his liberty, and he

died a free man in Africa.

Extension: Have small groups of students discuss the
characteristics of heroism. Ask them to identify and
comment upon adverbs that come up during the discussion.

Using *Good* and *Well*

- *Good* is an adjective and is used to describe nouns.

- *Well* is an adverb that tells *how* about a verb.

- Do not confuse the adjective *good* with the adverb *well*.

Read both sentences in each pair. Circle the letter of the sentence that uses *good* or *well* correctly.

1. **a.** The crew did not treat the captives good.

   b. The crew did not treat the captives well.

2. **a.** People on the *Amistad* did not eat well.

   b. People on the *Amistad* did not eat good.

3. **a.** The slaves fought well for their freedom.

   b. The slaves fought good for their freedom.

4. **a.** Cinqué fought for a well cause.

   b. Cinqué fought for a good cause.

5. **a.** Many good people helped abolish slavery.

   b. Many well people helped abolish slavery.

Write *well* or *good* to complete each sentence correctly. Then underline the word that *well* or *good* describes.

6. Would John Quincy Adams be a _____ lawyer for the Africans?

7. The former President wondered if he would do _____.

8. When the time came, he spoke _____ for the Mende.

9. Adams was a _____ judge of character.

10. Like the American patriots, he explained, they had fought _____ for freedom.

Extension: Challenge students to write a poem about
Cinqué's voyage home. Ask them to use the
descriptive words *good* and *well* in their poems.

164

Grade 5/Unit 6
Amistad Rising 10

Adverbs

Rewrite each sentence twice. Each time, add an adverb that tells when, where, or how.

1. The ship sails.

_____

_____

2. Cinqué fought.

_____

_____

3. Slave owners worked.

_____

_____

4. The waves are rising.

_____

_____

5. The judge spoke.

_____

_____

B. Write *well* or *good* to complete each sentence correctly.

6. During the storm, the ship did not travel _____.

7. A courageous leader is a _____ role model.

8. The ship's food did not taste _____.

9. John Quincy Adams argued _____ for the defense.

10. He was a _____ lawyer.

Adverbs

> • An **adverb** is a word that tells more about a verb, an adjective, or another adverb.
>
> • An adverb can tell *how*, *when*, or *where* an action takes place.

Mechanics

> • *Good* is an adjective and is used to describe nouns. *Well* is a adverb that tells *how* about a verb. Do not confuse the adjective *good* with the adverb *well*.

Write *well* or *good* to complete the sentences correctly. Underline the word that each *well* or *good* describes. Then draw a picture about the sentences.

1. The ship sailed _____.

2. A strong wind is _____ for sailing.

3. The *Amistad* sailed _____, for it was a _____ ship.

4. The Africans aboard the ship were not treated _____.

Adverbs That Compare

> - An adverb can compare two or more actions.
> - Add *-er* to most short adverbs to compare two actions.
> - Add *-est* to most short adverbs to compare more than two actions.

Read the sentences. Write the correct form of the adverb in parentheses.

1. (long) Of the many storms this season, this storm raged _____ of all.

2. (hard) Lightning hit _____ on the hill than in the valley.

3. (high) The mountains rose _____ than the mesa.

4. (long) Rip slept _____ than he ever had before.

5. (long) In fact, Rip slept _____ of all.

6. (hard) Dame Van Winkle worked _____ than Rip.

7. (fast) Rip ran _____ than he walked.

8. (early) The ship's bell rang _____ the second time.

9. (early) Wolf left the mountain _____ than Rip did.

10. (late) Rip left the mountain _____ of all.

11. (near) The thunder boomed _____ than a few minutes ago.

12. (soon) Rip wished that he had gotten up _____ than he did.

Extension: Ask students to compare two actions with the following adverbs: *hard, short, fast*. Then ask them to compare three or more actions with the same adverbs.

Adverbs That Compare

- Use *more* or *most* to form comparisons with adverbs that end in *-ly* or most other adverbs with two or more syllables.

- Use *more* to compare two actions; use *most* to compare more than two.

- When you use *more* or *most*, do not use the ending *-er* or *-est*.

Read the sentences. Write the correct form of the adverb in parentheses.

1. (slowly) Rip walked _____ than Wolf.

2. (quietly) Rip spoke _____ to children than his wife did.

3. (impatiently) Dame Van Winkle speaks the _____ of all.

4. (closely) Rip looked _____ around him than he had looked a minute ago.

5. (shyly) Of all the villagers, Little Rip greeted Rip _____ .

Read each sentence. If the adverb is correct, write Correct on the line. If it is not correct, rewrite the sentence so that the adverb will be correct.

6. The people shouted angrilier at Rip than they did at Wolf.

_____

7. The whistle played more beautifully than the last one played.

_____

8. That man sleeps more quietly of all.

_____

9. Rip answered most soonest of all the husbands.

_____

10. The thunder clapped more violenter than it had the last time.

_____

Extension: Have students write descriptions of a character in the play. Ask them to compare his or her actions to those of other villagers. Students should exchange descriptions and proofread for correct use of adverbs that compare.

168

Grade 5/Unit 6
Rip Van Winkle 10

Adverbs That Compare

- An adverb can compare two or more actions.
- Add *-er* to most short adverbs to compare two actions. Add *-est* to most short adverbs to compare more than two actions.
- Add *more* or *most* to form comparisons with adverbs that end in *-ly* or most other adverbs with two or more syllables. Use *more* to compare two actions; use *most* to compare more than two. When you use *more* or *most*, do not use the ending *-er* or *-est*.

Circle the adverbs in these paragraphs. Then write the paragraphs correctly.

Rip Van Winkle lived near the Catskill Mountains. These mountains rise highest than the land around them, and the storms rage more fiercer as you climb more higher on the slope. In the summer, thunderstorms arrive frequenter and lightning strikes most violentest than in the winter.

Today, the Hudson River passes through much of New York State. It runs slowlier as it falls lowly to flat land. As it passes New York City, the river runs slower of all.

Many years ago, people worked more harder than today to ship goods upstate. Ships from New York Harbor carried cargo more efficienter than mules did. Today, trucks and trains travel more speedier and most cheaply than ships do. In the years ahead, the river will continue to be importanter to people.

_____

_____

_____

_____

_____

_____

_____

_____

_____

_____

_____

10 Grade 5/Unit 6
Rip Van Winkle

Extension: Invite pairs or groups of students to create and present a story about a local storm. Suggest that they include a local historical figure in their stories. Ask students to include at least five adverbs that compare.

169

Using More and Most

> • Never add *-er* and *more* to the same adverb.
>
> • Never add *-est* and *most* to the same adverb.

Read each sentence. If the sentence uses *more* and *most* correctly, write **Correct**. Otherwise, rewrite the sentence to make the use of *more* and *most* correct.

1. The thunder pealed more loudlier every minute.

_____

2. The wind blew more fiercer than it had before.

_____

3. The river rose more fitfullier than it fell.

_____

4. Rip Van Winkle slept most soundest of all.

_____

5. Dame Van Winkle talked more loudly than other people.

_____

6. Rip's wife died more earlier than he did.

_____

7. Hendrik Hudson played ninepins most loudest of all.

_____

8. Is this the story told most frequently of New York's local legends?

_____

9. The high school group performed the play more professionaller than our class did.

_____

_____

10. Rip climbed more higher and more quicker than he expected.

_____

Adverbs That Compare

Choose the sentence in each group that is written incorrectly. Circle the letter of the incorrect sentence.

1. **a.** The children work more diligently than their father does.

   b. The children work most diligently than their father does.

   c. The children work most diligently of all.

2. **a.** Wolf comes more readily to Rip than he does to Dame.

   b. Wolf comes most readily to Rip than to Dame.

   c. Wolf comes more readily to Rip than even the children do.

3. **a.** Rip works more lovingly with children than he does with his wife.

   b. Of all the men in the village, Rip works most lovingly with the children.

   c. Rip works most lovingly with children than he does with his wife.

4. **a.** Rip slept longest than he worked.

   b. Rip slept longer than he worked.

   c. Rip slept longest of all.

5. **a.** Judith stared hardest at Rip than Doolittle did.

   b. Of all the villagers, Judith stared hardest at Rip.

   c. Judith stared harder at Rip than Doolittle did.

B. Choose the comparing adverb that best completes the sentence. Circle the letter of your answer.

6. Hendrik Hudson plays ninepins _____ than he sings.

   a. loudest

   b. louder

   c. more louder

7. Hendrik Hudson dances _____ today than yesterday.

   a. most merrily

   b. more merrier

   c. more merrily

8. The Hudson River flows _____ in the spring than in the summer.

   a. rapidest

   b. most rapidly

   c. more rapidly

Adverbs That Compare

- Add *-er* to most short adverbs to compare two actions. Add *-est* to most short adverbs to compare more than two actions.

- Add *more* or *most* to form comparisons with adverbs that end in *-ly* or most other adverbs with two or more syllables. Use *more* to compare two actions; use *most* to compare more than two.

- Never add *-er* and *more* or *-est* and *most* to the same adverb.

With a partner, take turns reading these sentences aloud. Listen for adverb errors. Together, rewrite the sentences to correct the errors.

1. No one reads the news most entertainingly than Derrick Van Bummel does.

_____

2. Afterward, the men talked more angrilier about British taxes than before.

_____

3. Rip Van Winkle played frequenter than he worked.

_____

4. The children talked to Rip most easiest of all.

_____

5. The odd sailor spoke most gruffly than Rip had expected.

_____

6. Never had Rip slept soundest than he did that night.

_____

7. Rip changed more dramatic of all sleepers.

_____

8. Who acted more strangelier—Rip or the people at the Union Hotel?

_____

Negatives

- A negative is a word that means "no," such as *not*, *never*, *nobody*, *nowhere*, and contractions with *n't*.
- Do not use two negatives in the same sentence.
- You can fix a sentence with two negatives by removing one.

Correct the sentences by removing one of the negatives.

1. Fresh water doesn't have no salt.

_____

2. Kiyomi's mother doesn't seem to have no fear.

_____

3. Kiyomi won't use no rope.

_____

4. The older girls didn't choose no diving.

_____

5. The waves didn't make no trouble.

_____

6. Soon, working underwater won't cause no problems.

_____

7. Some turtle eggs don't have no chance.

_____

8. The other turtles don't have no stars.

_____

9. Kiyomi won't keep no turtles.

_____

10. We can't see no clouds, today.

_____

Extension: Ask partners to write sentences about beaches, using two negatives in each sentence. Then ask them to correct each other's sentences by removing one negative.

Negatives

> • You can correct a sentence with two negatives by changing one negative to a positive word.

Negative	Positive
no, none	any
never	ever
nothing	anything
nobody	anybody
no one	anyone
nowhere	anywhere

Rewrite the sentences. Look for sentences with two negatives. Use a positive word in place of one of the negatives.

1. We never have no sea turtles where we live.

_____

2. Fish don't have lungs nowhere.

_____

3. Flounders don't have no eyes on one side.

_____

4. The baby turtles didn't never hesitate.

_____

5. Sharks won't eat none of these turtles.

_____

6. We didn't see whales nowhere.

_____

7. The girl has never found no pearls.

_____

8. Kiyomi didn't have no problems diving.

_____

Extension: Ask students to proofread recent writing assignments, looking for double negatives.

Negatives

> - A negative is a word that means "no," such as *not, never, nobody, nowhere,* and contractions with *n't.*
> - Do not use two negatives in the same sentence.
> - You can fix a sentence with two negatives by removing one.
> - You can correct a sentence with two negatives by changing one negative to a positive word.

Read each group of sentences. Cross out the sentence that is incorrect.

1. The sea is never calm in this bay.

   The sea is not ever calm in this bay.

   The sea is not never calm in this bay.

2. The girl never dove for abalone with nobody.

   The girl never dove for abalone with anybody.

   The girl dove for abalone with nobody.

3. There weren't never so many turtles before.

   There were never so many turtles here before.

   There weren't ever so many turtles before.

4. I don't see any good places to dive today.

   I don't see no good places to dive today.

   I see no good places to dive today.

Read the sentences. Rewrite each one two different ways.

5. The sun don't never shine in these caves.

   _____

   _____

6. There aren't no octopuses or abalone in the bay.

   _____

   _____

7. We didn't catch nothing today.

   _____

   _____

8. The turtles aren't nowhere near here today.

   _____

   _____

8 Grade 5/Unit 6
Sea Maidens of Japan

Extension: Ask partners to write dialogues about what doesn't happen on a beach. Ask them to write at least four negative sentences, using negatives correctly.

175

Contractions and Apostrophes

> • A contraction is a shortened form of two words.
>
> • A contraction may be formed by combining a verb with the word *not*.
>
> • An apostrophe (') shows where one or more letters have been left out.

isn't	is not	doesn't	does not
aren't	are not	didn't	did not
wasn't	was not	couldn't	could not
can't	cannot	wouldn't	would not
don't	do not	shouldn't	should not

Rewrite each sentence correctly. Use a contraction for every underlined pair of words. Correct any double negatives.

1. I <u>do not</u> travel to Japan no more.

_____

2. There <u>are not</u> no turtle nests under those trees.

_____

3. Sea turtles <u>were not</u> protected until recently.

_____

4. You <u>should not</u> bother no turtles on the beach.

_____

5. We <u>could not</u> never swim the length of this bay.

_____

6. The ama <u>is not</u> coming up for air yet.

_____

7. <u>Does not</u> no one want to practice diving?

_____

8. My ancestors <u>did not</u> come from nowhere near Tokyo.

_____

Extension: Ask students to write a poem about the sea turtle. Ask them to use three of the above contractions in their poems. Invite students to read their poems aloud for the class.

Negatives and Contractions

A. If the sentence is correct, write correct on the line. If it is not correct, rewrite it correctly.

1. Please don't bother no wild sea creatures.

_____

2. The sea isn't never as stormy as it was yesterday.

_____

3. The job of an ama is not easy.

_____

4. The ama must not do nothing but look for abalone.

_____

5. My sister isn't going to work as no ama no more.

_____

B. Write contractions for the following pairs of words.

6. can not _____

7. does not _____

8. should not _____

9. are not _____

10. could not _____

11. would not _____

12. did not _____

Contractions

- A contraction is a shortened form of two words.
- A contraction can be made by combining a verb with the word *not*.
- An apostrophe (') shows where one or more letters have been left out.

can't	cannot
don't	do not
doesn't	does not
didn't	did not
couldn't	could not
wouldn't	would not
shouldn't	should not

Look at the picture. Rewrite the paragraph on the lines below. Use contractions where possible and fix any double negatives.

The sea turtle is not a small turtle. It has a hard shell and tough flippers. The female does not stay long on land after she lays eggs. When the babies hatch, they do not hesitate at all. They know they should not stay nowhere on land. They would not want to be eaten by dogs or birds.

_____

_____

_____

_____

_____

Prepositions

> - A **preposition** comes before a noun or pronoun and relates that noun or pronoun to another word in the sentence.
> - Common prepositions are *about, above, across, after, at, behind, down, for, from, in, near, of, on, over, to, with.*

Read each sentence. Underline the prepositions. There may be more than one in each sentence.

1. Craig walked behind his father.

2. The bus traveled slowly on the highway.

3. The tired bus stalled near the Capitol.

4. Papa knew that peace came only with freedom.

5. On election day, Papa voted in town.

6. Craig waited in the hallway with his father.

7. Everyone climbed off the bus.

8. Papa stayed out late at night.

9. At least, we received a lot of votes.

10. Craig's family was worried about bombs.

11. Across the room, a congressman spoke about justice.

12. The gallery is there, above the main floor.

13. After awhile, we had seats in the gallery.

14. The congressperson spoke over the loudspeaker.

Extension: Invite students to write and deliver speeches on civil rights. Ask them to circle prepositions in their written copies.

Prepositional Phrases

> • A prepositional phrase is a group of words that begins with a preposition and ends with a noun or pronoun.
>
> • The object of a preposition is the noun or pronoun that follows the preposition.

Underline the preposition in each sentence. Circle the object of the preposition.

1. We wonder who is seated in Congress.

2. A congressperson spoke to us.

3. Mama said good-bye from the door.

4. The old bus made it all the way with all its problems.

5. Congresspeople walked through the tunnel.

6. Equality means one vote for every adult.

7. Craig spoke up above the noise.

8. Some congresspeople were on our side.

Complete each sentence with a prepositional phrase.

9. _____, it was cold and rainy.

10. Craig's family wanted to talk _____.

11. No one would let them sit _____.

12. Civil rights are important _____.

13. Craig was proud _____.

14. They were sent to wait _____.

15. Craig stood up _____.

Extension: Ask students to rewrite sentences 9 through 15, adding at least one more prepositional phrase to each sentence.

180

Grade 5/Unit 6
The Silent Lobby /15

Prepositions and Prepositional Phrases

- A **preposition** comes before a noun or pronoun and relates that noun or pronoun to another word in the sentence.
- Common prepositions are *about, above, across, after, at, behind, down, for, from, in, near, of, on, over, to, with*.
- A **prepositional phrase** is a group of words that begins with a preposition and ends with a noun or pronoun.
- The object of a preposition is the noun or pronoun that follows the preposition.

Underline the prepositional phrase in each sentence. Write the object of the preposition on the line.

1. Craig fought the good fight for freedom. _____

2. An old bus might never make it to the city. _____

3. Papa put his arm around Craig's shoulders. _____

4. The civil rights movement was a struggle in the South. _____

5. Today every American can vote on Election Day. _____

6. Across the road, Craig saw the Capitol. _____

7. Near the Capitol, a crowd gathered. _____

Complete the sentences with prepositional phrases.

8. _____, some Congresspeople changed their minds.

9. Craig learned a valuable lesson _____.

10. _____, the bus had engine trouble.

11. _____, there seemed to be no hope.

12. Craig sat _____.

Extension: Have students write ten sentences, each with at least one prepositional phrase. Have them underline the prepositional phrases.

Commas and Prepositional Phrases

- A prepositional phrase may come at the beginning of a sentence.

- Put a comma after a prepositional phrase composed of four or more words that comes at the beginning of a sentence.

Read the essay. Place commas where they are needed.

Before the civil rights movement life was hard in many black communities. In the southern states African-Americans were turned away from many restaurants and stores. On city buses African-Americans had to sit in the back. At many voting polls African-Americans were forced to take unfair tests. Even in the public schools African American students were treated unfairly.

Martin Luther King was a champion of civil rights. He knew every American should have the chance to vote. He believed all people should attend decent schools and be able to use public transportation restrooms, and restaurants. Soon many people were marching. Over the entire United States people spoke up for equality. With such a strong public protest changes were bound to take place. After a long hard struggle the Civil Rights Act was passed.

Prepositions

Circle the letter of the preposition that fits best in each sentence.

1. Craig's community fought _____ civil rights.

   a. near

   b. for

   c. at

2. The Capitol is _____ Washington, D.C.

   a. in

   b. over

   c. under

3. The struggle against prejudice continues _____ America.

   a. of

   b. before

   c. across

4. People everywhere fought _____ violence.

   a. to

   b. without

   c. of

5. Please give this letter _____ the congressperson.

   a. after

   b. near

   c. to

6. Craig was a young boy _____ the south.

   a. from

   b. after

   c. with

7. Papa knew a lot _____ prejudice.

   a. across

   b. with

   c. about

8. We trust our congressperson will vote _____ our cause.

   a. over

   b. of

   c. for

Commas and Prepositional Phrases

- A preposition comes before a noun or pronoun and relates that noun or pronoun to another word in the sentence.
- Common prepositions are *about, above, across, after, at, behind, down, for, from, in, near, of, on, over, to, with*.
- A prepositional phrase is a group of words that begins with a preposition and ends with a noun or pronoun.
- Put a comma after a prepositional phrase composed of four or more words that comes at the beginning of a sentence.
- The object of a preposition is the noun or pronoun that follows the preposition.

Work with a partner. As one of you reads the sentences aloud, the other proofreads. Look for a place in each sentence that needs a comma. Rewrite the sentences, adding the missing commas.

1. In the late afternoon the bus rolled into the city.

   _____

2. Across the crowded hall congresspeople argued.

   _____

3. Below the city streets there is a tunnel.

   _____

4. After the hard struggle voting rights were won.

   _____

5. Through this entire experience Craig learned a lot.

   _____

Sentence Combining

> • Two sentences can be combined by adding an adjective or adverb to one sentence.

Combine each pair of sentences. Remember to leave out words that repeat or mean the same thing.

1. The Amazon is a wild forest. The Amazon is enormous.

_____

2. Many rivers cross this forest. The rivers are wide.

_____

3. We heard the bad news. We heard it yesterday.

_____

4. People who cut trees must pay fines. The fines are huge.

_____

5. Satellites provide information. The information is crucial.

_____

6. Satellites provide crucial information. They provide it quickly.

_____

7. The Indians like their lives. Their lives are traditional.

_____

8. The rainforest is a national treasure. The rainforest is important.

_____

9. Indians live in the jungle. Indians live peacefully.

_____

10. The 1990s were destructive years. The years were terrible.

_____

Extension: Ask partners to write short sentences about the rainforest. Than have them exchange papers and combine sentences that share a noun or verb.

Sentence Combining

> • Two sentences can be combined by adding a prepositional phrase to one sentence.

Read the pair of sentences. Combine each pair, using a prepositional phrase.

1. The Yanomami live traditionally. The Yanomami live in the Amazon.

_____

2. People cut trees. The trees are cut for fuel and lumber.

_____

3. The rain hits the ground. The rain hits during the night.

_____

4. Piranha eat other fish. Piranha eat in the Amazon River.

_____

5. Deforestation threatens life. Deforestation threatens around the world.

_____

6. Environmentalists protect the rainforest. They work in Brazil.

_____

7. Parrots live nearby. Parrots live in the canopy.

_____

8. Farmers plant crops. Farmers plant near the rainforest.

_____

9. Environmentalists appreciate Possuelo. They appreciate his hard work.

_____

10. The rivers run full. The rivers run across the jungle.

_____

Extension: Ask partners to give each other topics related to the rainforest. Have each student write four sentences about the topic. Then challenge partners to write as many combinations of the sentences as they can.

Grade 5/Unit 6
Amazon Alert! /10

Sentence Combining

> • Two sentences can be combined by adding an adjective or adverb to one sentence.
>
> • Two sentences can be combined by adding a prepositional phrase to one sentence.

Read each paragraph. Look for sentences that can be combined. Choose the best way to combine the sentences as you rewrite the paragraphs.

The jungle has many animals and plants. The animals and plants are diverse. Scientists have not counted even half of their numbers. People study the rainforest. They study it continually. Some plants can be used for medicines. These plants are in the rainforest. Some plants can cure diseases. The diseases are serious.

_____

_____

_____

_____

_____

People can protect the rainforest. The rainforest is fragile. You can recycle paper and wood. You can recycle in your home. Architects can build with steel. They can build often. If you care a lot, you can also call an environmental group. You can call soon. You can save the trees. The trees are in the rainforest.

_____

_____

_____

_____

_____

_____

Extension: Ask students to write two versions of a poem about forests. Have them write one version that contains small choppy sentences and stanzas. Have them write another version by combining shorter sentences.

Using Punctuation Marks

> • Begin every sentence with a capital letter.
>
> • Use the correct end mark for each sentence.
>
> • Use a comma to set off a person's name when the person is spoken to directly.

Rewrite the sentences. Add capitalization, end punctuation, and commas where they are needed.

1. martin have you ever been to the rainforest

   _____

2. our plane landed in Sao Paulo

   _____

3. there are so many beautiful flowers there

   _____

4. this jungle is incredible

   _____

5. anita can you tell me the name of that bird

   _____

6. the canopy is full of light

   _____

7. jennifer look at the monkeys

   _____

8. kito what are you photographing

   _____

9. dad I can't see where you are pointing

   _____

10. i want to visit the Amazon rainforest

    _____

Extension: Have partners write funny statements, exclamations, and questions about monkeys. Ask them to omit capitalization, end punctuation, and commas. Then have partners correct each other's writing.

Grade 5/Unit 6
Amazon Alert! / 10

Sentence Combining and Using Punctuation Marks

A. Combine each pair of sentences. Write the new sentence on the line.

1. Monkeys eat bananas. Monkeys eat in the treetops.

_____

2. Monkeys play tricks. The tricks are funny.

_____

3. People build houses. People build with wood.

_____

4. The Amazon has trees. The trees are incredible.

_____

5. Indians gather plants. Indians gather in the rainforest.

_____

6. The Yanomami have hunted animals. The Yanomami have hunted for centuries.

_____

7. People breathe oxygen. People breathe into their lungs.

_____

B. Rewrite each sentence. Add punctuation and capitals.

8. Fernando will you write about the rainforest

_____

9. these birds are amazing

_____

10. amy there are orchids in this forest

_____

11. what do the birds eat

_____

12. Delia watch out for that snake

_____

Sentence Combining

> • Two sentences can be combined by adding an adjective or adverb to one sentence.
> • Two sentences can be combined by adding a prepositional phrase to one sentence.

Mechanics

> • Begin every sentence with a capital letter.
> • Use the correct end mark for each sentence.
> • Use a comma to set off a person's name when the person is spoken to directly.

Read the sentences about the picture. Combine the sentences by adding an adverb, adjective, or prepositional phrase to one sentence.

1. The canopy shades the forest. The canopy shades everywhere.

   _____

2. The leaves make oxygen. The leaves are green.

   _____

3. The sun warms the earth. The sun warms in the daytime.

   _____

Rewrite the sentences with the correct punctuation.

4. molly did you hear the parrot call

   _____

5. this place is so beautiful

   _____

6. I don't like the snakes Juan do you

   _____

7. maria, look at the beautiful butterflies

   _____

8. we should come back next year

   _____

Adverbs

Read each passage and look at the underlined sentences. If the sentence is incorrect or can be written more clearly, choose the best way to rewrite it. Circle the letter of the correct answer.

> <u>In the 1800s, many people fought fierce for African American freedom.</u> These
> (1)
> people wanted to end slavery. They were called abolitionists. <u>Abolitionists in the</u>
>
> <u>North and the South believed strongly in equality.</u> Their hard struggle helped to
> (2)
> set enslaved people free.

1. **A** In the 1800s, many people fought fiercelly for African American freedom.

   B In the 1800s, many people fought fiercely for African American freedom.

   C in the 1800s, many people fiercely for African American freedom.

   D No mistake.

2. **F** Abolitionists in the North and the South believed rightly in equality.

   G Abolitionists in the North and the South believed exactly in equality.

   H Abolitionists in the North and the South believed sometimes in equality.

   J No mistake.

> As Rip Van Winkle slept, the storm raged more terribly every minute. <u>The wind</u>
>
> <u>blew most wildly than before.</u> <u>The thunder boomed more louder than cannons.</u>
> (3)   (4)
> Meanwhile, Rip slept the most peacefully of anyone.

3. **A** The wind blew more wildly than before.

   B The wind blew more wilder than before.

   C The wind blew most wildest than before.

   D No mistake.

4. **F** The thunder boomed most louder than cannons.

   G The thunder boomed louder than cannons.

   H The thunder boomed loudest than cannons.

   J No mistake.

Adverbs

> On our vacation, my sister and I went snorkeling in Mexico. We wanted to
> see snapping turtles. We also hoped to see some dolphins. <u>But we couldn't see</u>
>   (5)
> <u>nothing the first day.</u> <u>It looked like there were none nowhere in the bay.</u> Mom told us
>   (6)
> to try again tomorrow. So we spent the afternoon looking for shells on the beach.

5. **A** But we couldn't see none the first day.

    B But we could see anything the first day.

    C But we couldn't see anything the first day.

    D No mistake.

6. **F** It looked like there were no nowhere in the bay.

    G It looked like there weren't none nowhere in the bay.

    H It looked like there were none anywhere in the bay.

    J No mistake.

> <u>You can write a letter. You can write to your congressperson.</u> Congresspeople
>   (7)
> expect to get letters from adults and students. <u>We wrote letters. We wrote them</u>
>   (8)
> <u>yesterday.</u> Our class wrote our ideas about the rainforest and equal rights.

7. **A** You can write a letter, you can write to your congressperson.

    B You can write a letter to your congressperson.

    C You write to your congressperson.

    D No mistake.

8. **F** We wrote letters yesterday.

    G We wrote letters them yesterday.

    H We wrote letters we wrote them yesterday.

    J No mistake.